A HISTORY OF PARASITOLOGY

PRINTED IN GREAT BRITAIN

A HISTORY OF
PARASITOLOGY

BY

W. D. FOSTER
M.D.Cantab., M.C.Path.
Professor of Medical Microbiology
Makerere University College

E. & S. LIVINGSTONE LTD.
EDINBURGH AND LONDON
1965

To

EDETE AND PETER

PREFACE

THERE is no book on the history of parasitology in English and I am not aware of one in any other language. This gap in the literature I have tried to fill in outline. My plan has been to give an introductory chapter on the general development of parasitology from ancient times to about 1850, then to illustrate the subject by giving an account of the development of our knowledge of a limited number of parasites chosen because investigations related to them opened up new fields in parasitology. Thus study of the cestodes and the liver fluke first led to the concept of alternation of host species. Manson's work on *Wuchereria bancrofti* drew attention to the transmission of parasites by biting arthropods, the study of hookworm demonstrated yet another type of parasitic life-cycle and so on.

The period covered is from ancient times to about 1920, by which time parasitology was a well-established branch of biology. This has led to the omission of much interesting work which might have been included, for example, the discovery of the exo-erythrocytic cycle of the malaria parasites but, in general, I felt that to sift the more modern work and assess its relative importance would need a professional parasitologist, which I am not. This book, it is hoped, gives an accurate account of the history of the basic discoveries in parasitology at a level which is comprehensible to the non-professional parasitologist.

I should like to thank the various people who have helped in the preparation of this book. My wife performed the tedious task of converting a rough manuscript to typescript and to her my best thanks are due. My colleague Dr. David Bradley and Dr. Jean Théodoridès have read the whole of the book which has much benefited by their comments. The illustrations were provided partly from the Wellcome collections through the kindness of Dr. F. N. L. Poynter and others were prepared by Mr. R. Wellingham from books in the author's possession. I am also indebted to Makerere University College Publications and Research Fund for a grant towards the expenses of publication. Finally, I should like to thank my publishers in the persons of Mr. William Macmillan and Mr. Charles Macmillan for encouragement and help.

W. D. F.

Makerere University College,
January, 1965.

CONTENTS

CHAPTER I

PARASITOLOGY FROM ANCIENT TIMES UNTIL THE MIDDLE OF THE NINETEENTH CENTURY

SOME knowledge of the common parasites must go back to prehistoric times as it is unthinkable that some of the intestinal worms and ectoparasites such as fleas and lice went unnoticed. Indeed knowledge in prehistoric times probably corresponded to that of primitive races inhabiting some parts of the world today. An investigation carried out by Hoeppli among primitive tribes in Sarawak and North Borneo showed that the majority of persons questioned were familiar with at least two types of intestinal worm—probably *Ascaris* and *Enterobius* and some had a knowledge of tapeworms. They had no clear idea as to whether these worms were different species of animals and the general opinion prevailed that the small gradually changed into larger ones.[1]

In ancient Egypt little was known about parasites except that they existed and the well known medical papyrus, Papyrus Ebers, mentions intestinal worms and some forms of ectoparasites. Clinically the ancient Egyptians were familiar with the most important parasitic disease of their country, schistosomiasis, but were not, of course, acquainted with its parasitic nature, although there was a general conception that many diseases were due to parasites.

There is evidence of a much more extensive knowledge of parasites amongst the scientists of ancient Greece and Rome. Aristotle was familiar with the helminths of dogs, fishes and the *Cysticercus cellulosae* of pigs which he compared to hailstones. The frequent occurrence of these cysts in the tongues of pigs was sufficiently well known to be alluded to in a comedy by Aristophanes. The guinea-worm was well known and its frequency in the people on the shores of the Red Sea was appreciated over a hundred years before Christ. It has been suggested that the Mosaic prohibitions on certain animals as food for the Israelites was based on a knowledge that they were infested with parasites and that the plague of fiery serpents that afflicted them during their wanderings was an outbreak of guinea-worm infestation.[2] But for this opinion the relevant passages in the Old Testament afford little evidence. Regarding the guinea-worm, Paulus Aegineta remarked " In India and the upper parts of Egypt a class of worms called dracunculli, resembling the intestinal, are formed in the muscular parts of the body, such as the arms, thighs and legs and in the sides of children, under the skin ". He described how eventually a blister forms over the head of the worm which then emerges. This parasite was not however universally regarded as a living animal. Soranus in the second century A.D. thought it a " nervous concretion ". Galen also considered it to be nervous in origin and this view was even held by British surgeons working in India in the early nineteenth century.[3] Galen recognized three human species of intestinal worm, *Ascaris, Enterobius* and *Taenia* and knew which part of the intestine they inhabited.[4] During the later Roman Empire descriptions of parasites became more frequent and detailed. Some idea of their medical importance was gained and various speculations as to their nature and origin made. Aretaeus (A.D. 81-138) in discussing dropsy showed that he was familiar with hydatid disease. He wrote of dropsies confined to small areas such as the liver in which " small and numerous bladders full of fluid, are contained in the place where ascites is found; but they also float in a copious fluid of which this is proof; for if you perforate the abdomen so as to evacuate the fluid, after a small discharge of fluid, the bladder within will block up the passage; but if you push the instrument farther in, the discharge will be renewed ".[5] Paulus Aegineta (A.D. 625-690) described three sorts of worm inhabiting the human intestine, " the round, the broad and thirdly those called Ascarides. They are all the offspring of crude and thick pituitous matters with a suitable putrefaction, such matters collected in children, and others who take too much food ". By round worm he referred to the modern *Ascaris* which he regarded as the commonest type, was generated in the small intestine and often vomited. His "Ascarides " he described as resembling earthworms and said that they were " formed about the extremity of the rectum and the beginning of the sphincter ani, and occasioning a great itching of the parts ".

He must therefore be referring to threadworms. With regard to the broad worm he considered it " conversion of the membrane which lines the inside of the intestine into a living body " and wrote that " the most unerring symptom is when certain substances, like the seed of the gourd are discharged in the faeces ".[6]

The Arabs added nothing of importance to knowledge of helminths and were indeed responsible for the erroneous idea that the individual segments of tapeworms passed in the faeces were in fact a separate species of parasite named cucurbitini. They were of course familiar with the guinea-worm of which infestation Avicenna gave a good description noting that " the disease is commonest at Medina, whence it takes its name ".[7]

Few new important observations in parasitology were made until the seventeenth century but the literature of the Middle Ages is not devoid of references to the subject. In the thirteenth century, Albertus Magnus described parasitic worms from horses, dogs, falcons and fishes, but not sufficiently well to allow them to be identified.[8] A twelfth century nun, Hildegardis de Pinguia, seems to have been familiar with the mite of scabies. Sir Anthony Fitzherbert in his *A newe Treate or Treatyse most profytable for all Husbandemen* (1532) gave the first recognizable description of the liver fluke. Having described the various ways " to knowe rotten shape " he noted that " if thou cut the lyver, therein wyll be lytell quickens lyke flokes ".[9]

Although actual knowledge of parasites was limited, worms of various kinds were widely believed to be the cause of many diseases and a large number of wholly imaginary parasites were described, some of which were quite fantastic. Belief in the existence of the most amazing parasites was held even up to the eighteenth century by otherwise very competent helminthologists. Nor were parasites considered exclusively deleterious in their effects. The Chinese believed that a man should harbour at least three worms to remain in good health and in Europe in the eighteenth century the presence of worms in children was regarded as beneficial by many peoples.

In widely separated parts of the world toothache was regarded as being caused by a " toothworm ". The " heartworm " was a favourite explanation of a cause of sudden death. Ambroise Paré believed that many strange animals might be created in abscesses. The Chinese proposed a worm as the cause of phthisis to which the patient's soul became attached on death. The worm then left the patient's body and sought to invade a person of the same constitution as the deceased, namely the close relatives—a convenient explanation of the familial incidence of the disease. An umbilical worm was thought to be responsible for general weakness in some babies and even as late as the eighteenth century, the distinguished French parasitologist Nicolas Andry recommended, as a diagnostic test, that there be " fastened on the umbilicus of the children, one of those fishes which are called gudgeons, one finds on the following morning a part of this fish is corroded " having been eaten by the worm. Nose, eye, ear and urethral worms were described, some of which may not have been wholly imaginary, the possibility of the larvae of flies developing in already filthy and diseased areas being well known.[10]

From the sixteenth century onwards imaginary microparasites were regarded as the cause of many infectious diseases. Thus Ulrich von Hutten considered the possibility of syphilis being caused by small winged worms and Kircher's views on the aetiology of plague are well known. Minute animals were quite widely thought to be present in the saliva of rabid dogs and Hartsoeker in a letter to Andry at the end of the seventeenth century wrote " I believe that the worms cause most of the diseases which attack mankind ".[11] Besides belief in entirely imaginary parasites many erroneous ideas were held with regard to the possibility of various free-living animals inhabiting the human body and of actual parasites. There are many reports of animals such as frogs, toads, eels, lizards and snakes which are supposed to have lived in the stomach, intestine, urinary bladder, female genital organs and even abscesses. Indeed it is impossible to resist the conclusion that doctors were much misled by their malingering or hysterical patients who deliberately added various animals to their urine or faeces.

From ancient times until nearly the middle of the nineteenth century it was generally believed that parasites arose by spontaneous generation on or in the body. It is true that there were some workers who held that like other animals internal parasites could only develop from the eggs of parents like themselves but they were exceptional.

This view of the origin of parasites formed but a part of the much larger concept of spontaneous generation of living things in the whole realm of nature and the general doctrine must receive some attention. Internal parasites were regarded as very good examples of spontaneous generation and indeed it is difficult to blame a person for not having any other view of, say an encysted worm buried in the substances of the brain. Belief in the spontaneous generation of a variety of animals was world wide. Aristotle thought that a sort of vital spirit acting on decomposing material could give rise to many insects and worms. However, he recorded an observation, the first of many which were slowly to upset the whole idea of spontaneous generation, that "There are certain insects which, although formed by spontaneous generation nevertheless are male and female, and as a result of their copulations something is formed, though it is imperfect".[12] The list of animals regarded as spontaneously generated by authors of the ancient world is considerable and includes butterflies from dew, moths from wood and old clothes, mites from wax, bees from the carcasses of bulls, beetles from dead asses and snakes from the putrefying spinal cords of man.

It was not until the seventeenth century that any serious doubts were raised. William Harvey was doubtful of the possibility of spontaneous generation and is often credited with the doctrine "omne vivum ex ovo". But that he accepted the possibility of spontaneous generation seems clear for he wrote "Because this is common to all living creatures *viz.* that they derive their origin from either semen or eggs, whether this semen have proceeded from others of the same kind, or have come by chance from something else"[13]. Swammerdam as a result of his most accurate and detailed anatomical studies of the lower animals was firmly of the opinion that there was no such thing as spontaneous generation. He wrote "If anyone accurately considers the disposition and the structure of the smallest and largest animals, and compares them one with another, he will see that . . . they spring from like principles, which are eggs of their parents, as well in the smallest as largest animals . . . nor is there any creature excepted from this universal law of its origin".[14] Similarly Leeuwenhoek advanced arguments against the current opinion that weevils spontaneously generated in corn seed and undertook an experimental study clearly showing that this was not so. Redi disproved the belief that flies arose spontaneously from meat. In his *Esperienze intorno alla generazione degli insetti* of 1668 he wrote "Although content to be corrected by one wiser than myself, if I should make erroneous statements, I shall express my belief that the earth, after having brought forth the first plants and animals at the beginning by the order of the omnipotent creator, has never since produced any kinds of plants or animals either perfect or imperfect, and everything which we know in past or present times that she has produced, came solely from the true seeds of the plants and animals themselves . . . ".[15] He then goes on to give an account of his well known experiments showing that the larvae of flies failed to develop on meat from which adult flies were excluded although developing freely on exposed meat. However, even Redi could not account for the presence of gallflies other than by spontaneous generation and wrote " I cannot refrain from saying that I do not consider it a great sin against philosophy to maintain that the worms of plants are created by the same natural principle that produces the fruits of plants . . . ".[16] Dr. Thomas Browne raised a doubt as to whether mice can be procreated of putrefaction and was soundly taken to task by the author of *A refutation of Dr. Browne's vulgar errors* who amongst other things said " I have seen one whose belly by drinking puddle water was swelled to a vast capacity, being full of small toads, frogs, evets, and such vermin usually breed in putrefied water ".[17]

Edward Tyson made careful dissections of *Ascaris lumbricoides,* showed that the worms were of distinct sexes and drew the natural conclusion that they were generated by sexual reproduction. He wrote " The curious researches of many inquisitive persons after the manner of the generation of insects . . . have much advanced the doctrine of univocal generation. Yet one great difficulty remains with me, how to account for several of those that are bred in animal bodies; . . . But though we are gravel'd in assigning how first these sorts of worms should come into the body; yet being once there, there is nothing more plain, than that the *Lumbricus teres* is propagated by a univocal generation; there being in this sort so perfect a distinction of sexes, male and female . . . "[18] This recognition of distinct sexes in simple animals and in parasites, first alluded to by Aristotle, was the earliest observation to strike at the roots of the belief in spontaneous generation. For centuries its implication was evaded for although eventually it became freely admitted that parasites might reproduce sexually the origin of the original parasites was still considered to be by spontaneous generation. That this was Tyson's view is evident from the above quotation. Despite the well founded doubts expressed in the seventeeth century concerning spontaneous generation the contention of George Cheyne, writing in 1734, that " Nobody believes nowadays, that any animal, how abject soever, can be produced by an equivocal generation or without the conjunction of Male and Female Parents . . .", was hardly accurate.[19]

The influential Comte de Buffon certainly believed in spontaneous generation as did the great Albrecht Haller. Even as late as 1839 the anatomist Allen Thompson wrote that while he was "inclined to admit the existence of spontaneous generation amongst some species of cryptogamic plants, infusorial animalcules and entozoa, it must be held in recollection that many of these productions, after their first origin, propagate their species as parents—that the so-called spontaneous kind of generation is to be looked upon as no more than an exception to the general law of reproduction . . . ".[20]

Considering the doctrine of spontaneous generation more particularly as concerned with parasitology, although generally accepted by parasitologists of the eighteenth century, the problem began to be seriously discussed on the basis of the evidence available and it is of interest to follow some of the arguments. Andry did not believe in spontaneous generation of animals of any kind and thought that the presence of intestinal worms was due to the ingestion or inhalation of their seeds. This he considered to be supported by the recent revelations of the microscope and he clearly stated that man became infested with worms by eating or drinking food contaminated with seeds of worms from another man.[21] Two of the most distinguished parasitologists of the later eighteenth century, Bloch and Göze, both believed that parasites were inborn in their hosts and were rewarded by the Royal Society of Science of Copenhagen with a gold and silver medal respectively for their essays in support of their contention. Bloch was a doctor of medicine in Berlin and a member of numerous scientific societies. His treatise on the generation of intestinal worms was first published in German in 1782 and translated into French in 1788. Göze was a clergyman by profession, but an amateur naturalist with a European reputation, being a member of various naturalist's societies in Berlin, Helmstedt, Halle, Stockholm and Lund. He wrote by far the most comprehensive textbook of parasitology, of the eighteenth century, which we will consider later.[22] Bloch advanced 12 reasons for his view on the origin of parasites which may be summed up in the obvious adaptation of intestinal worms to their hosts, the fact that they were never found and indeed rapidly die outside the body and that they show considerable host specificity. He accounted for the enormous production of the eggs by intestinal worms because of their great risk of loss in the faeces and considers that the seeds of worms can hardly enter the host from outside because if this were so, intestinal worms would be more evenly distributed amongst animal species.[23]

Brera, professor of medicine at Pavia, writing in 1798, was opposed to the idea of spontaneous generation. He believed that worms developed from eggs taken in with the food but considered that they only developed in persons whose constitution was favourable to the worm. He also thought that the worms could be inborn to the extent that they were transmitted from mother to foetus *in utero,* quoting a case of three generations in one family all infested with worms to support this. He appears to have been the first to suggest that man might acquire some of his parasites from animals used as food, writing " Perhaps in time more happy observers will discover the eggs of the principal human worms in the bowels of the animals from which we take our daily food ".[24]

However, Olombel in his *Remarques sur les maladies vermineuses* published in 1816, having given a thorough review of the various opinions regarding the origin of parasitic worms, concluded that none of the current ideas was satisfactory. As late as 1819, Bremser wrote that since he regarded it as proved that simple animals such as infusoria could be generated from dead organic matter, such generation must take place more readily in living bodies and the creatures so generated would be more perfect. He went on " If we accept as proved that

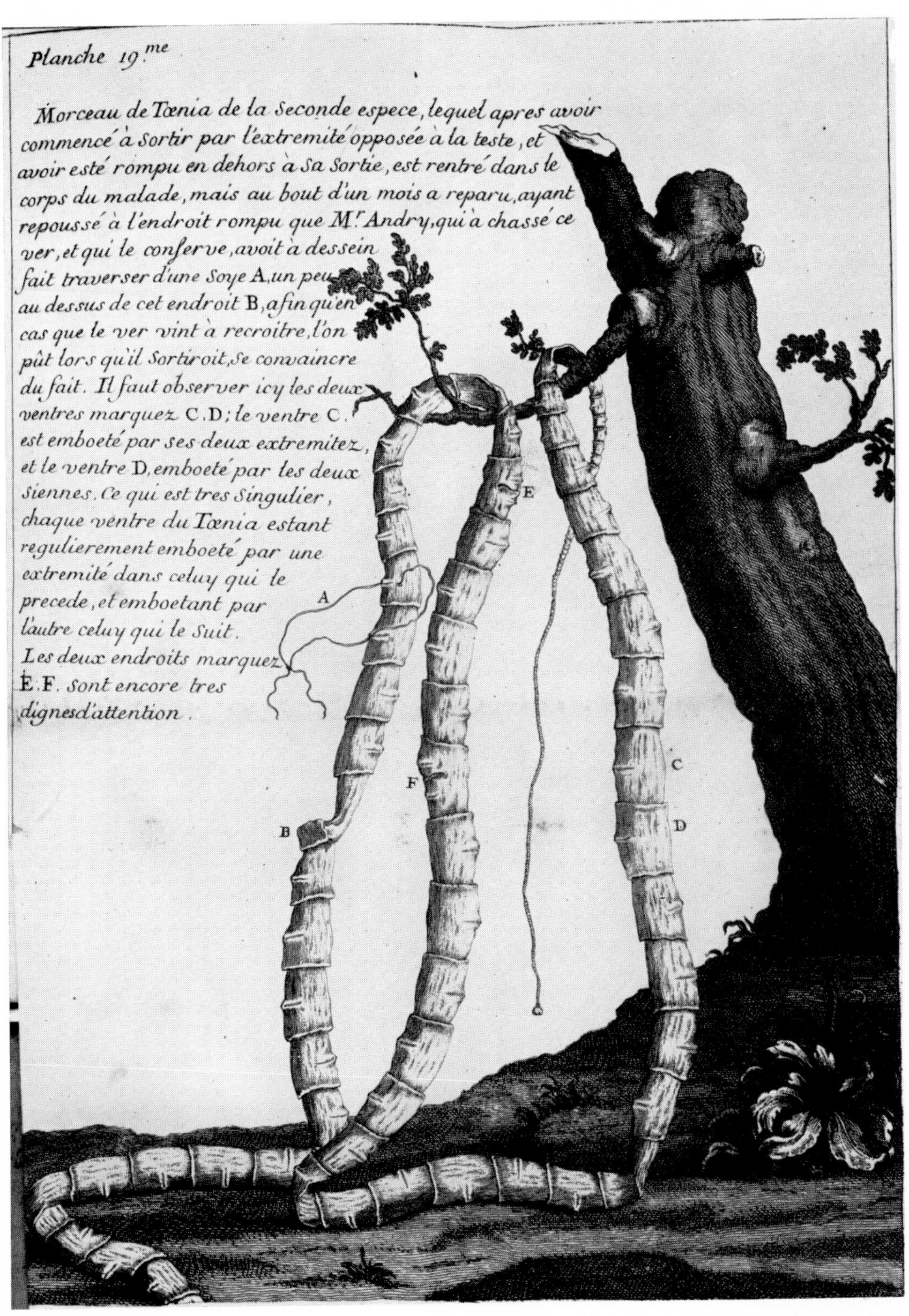

PLATE I
A tapeworm (from N. Andry, 1718).

[To face p. 8

PLATE II

Removing a guinea-worm (from Andry, 1741).

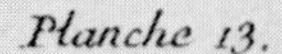

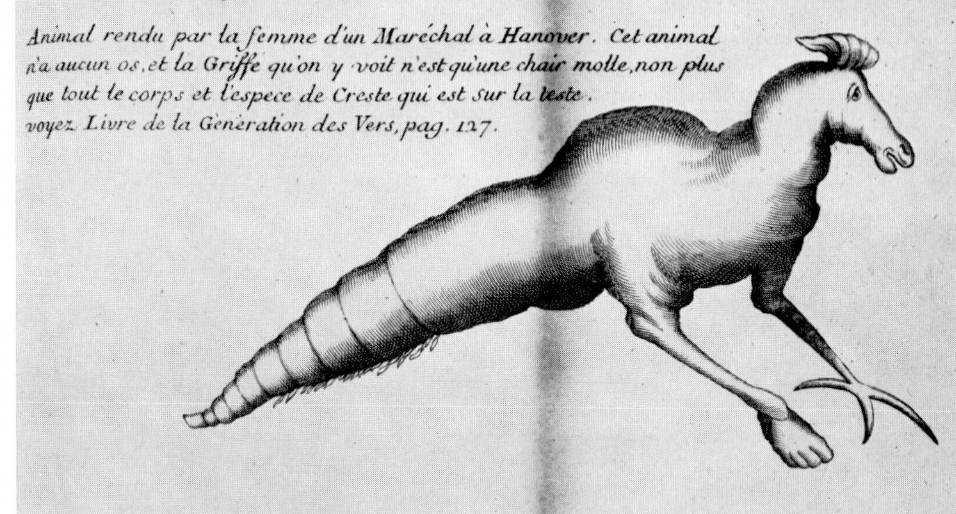

PLATE III

A piece of tapeworm, clearly Diphylobothrium and an alleged parasite (from Andry, 1718).

To face p. 9]

intestinal worms do not enter the body from outside and are not inborn, they therefore must owe their existence to spontaneous generation . . .", but he continued, "Worms once spontaneously generated in a body, if the cause which first stimulate the development and formation cease to exist, can generate and propagate by copulations, all our intestinal worms are provided with generative organs".[25] Indeed as Huxley pointed out, it was only between 1840 and 1870 that because "the splendid patience of von Siebold, von Beneden, Leuckart, Kuchenmeister and other helminthologists, has succeeded in tracing every such parasite, often through the strangest wanderings and metamorphoses to an egg derived from a parent" the doctrine of the spontaneous generation of parasites came to be finally abandoned.[26]

A useful idea of the general development of parasitology from the end of the seventeenth century to the middle of the nineteenth century may be obtained by a brief survey of the more important parasitological writings for this period. The earliest book to be devoted wholly to parasitology was the *Osservazioni intorni agli animali viventi che si trovano negli animali viventi* by Francesco Redi. Redi has been called the father of parasitology and in so far as such a title may be bestowed on anyone he is indeed worthy of it. Parasitological studies were but a part of his life work. He was born in 1626 in Arezzo of noble family and educated at Florence and Pisa. Quite early in life he was appointed physician to the Grand Duke of Tuscany and rapidly acquired a great reputation and received many honours. He was a good clinician, and a naturalist of wide interests as well as being a poet and linguist. During the last nine years of his life he suffered from epilepsy and died in 1697. Redi was particularly interested in ectoparasites and in work published in 1688 and 1671 described and figured lice and ticks from man and various domesticated animals. He showed his independent judgment by describing the louse of the donkey although Aristotle had definitely stated that that animal never harboured lice. He considerably advanced knowledge of the anatomy of lice, particularly of the generative organs, with important implications regarding their origin. He dissected many animals in his search for parasites, discovering a number of new species, and in his *Osservazioni* described a total of 108 different species. The book contains 25 plates in which many of the parasites are illustrated, including tapeworms from both dog and cat in which the scolex is illustrated for the first time. He, independently of Tyson, drew attention to the fact that *Ascaris* were either male or female, stressed the animal nature of bladder worms and had already in 1671 given the first illustration of *Fasciola hepatica*.[27]

In 1699 Nicolas Andry published a most important book entitled *De la génération des vers dans le corps de l'homme*. New editions followed in 1718 and 1741 and he also published a fine volume of plates to illustrate the text with the 1718 edition. Andry was born in 1658 and is best known as the originator of the word " orthopaedics " from the Greek for " straightening of children " but he was undoubtedly the most learned parasitologist of the early eighteenth century and held views in some respects in advance of many successors. Andry aimed to give a complete treatise on the internal parasites of man, how they develop, the different species, their clinical effects and their treatment. The work is prefaced by lengthy controversial letters of little interest as well as 14 letters of approbation from various eminent scientists. G. C. Fagon, physician to the king, to whom the book is dedicated, remarked, referring to Andry's treatment of the subject, " Un des plus vils animaux du monde y est examiné avec une si noble erudition que l'on perd d'abord l'idée de sa bassesse ". In the first chapter worms are defined from the zoological point of view, revealing the primitive state of zoological classification in the pre-Linnaean era . . . an important point when considering the many fantastic animals and artefacts to which a parasitic mode of life was attributed. Thus "worms" belong to the group " insect " which are segmented animals. " Insects " are divided into two groups large and small. The former includes snakes, frogs and scorpions and the latter the " worms " which include, besides the parasites, earthworms, snails, flies, ants and caterpillars.[28] The parasitic worms of man are divided into groups, those living outside the intestine which are further subdivided on an anatomical basis according to their site into Encéphales, Pulmonaires, Hépatiques, etc., and those living within the intestine. Intestinal worms are described as being of three sorts; long and short and flat. The first type dwells in the duodenum and is called *Strongyles* from the Greek for round and long and must correspond to the modern *Ascaris lumbricoides.* The second is found in the rectum and is called *Ascaris* again from the Greek for agitation because those little worms are always in active motion. Of the third, *Taenia,* Andry recognized two types, the first with what he called a " spine " running down the whole length of the middle of the worm. This can be seen from his illustrations, which are artistically of a high order, to be no more than a misrepresentation of the medially placed genital pore of *Bothriocephalus* and the segments can be seen to be broad and short although this character is not commented on in the textbook. The other type is described as having a little nodule at the edge of each segment and again it is clear from his illustrations that these are laterally placed genital pores of either *Taenia saginata* or *Taenia solium* or, most probably, both. Some of his illustrations suggest *T. saginata* with relatively long segments whilst others relatively shorter could be *T. solium.* Andry was the first to illustrate the scolex of a human tapeworm, that of *T. saginata.* He regarded the genital pores as pulmonary openings through which the tapeworm took in air, was aware of, and well illustrated, the ramifications of the uterus but regarded this as a tracheal system and compared it with the tracheal system of the silk-worm described by Malpighi.[29] Two erroneous opinions relating to tapeworms he corrected; that there was a third species the cucurbitini which he rightly recognized as merely a few segments of a tapeworm and that tapeworms were not individuals but animals composed of an agglomeration of numerous individuals. This view he dismissed because of the presence of the single head.

He dealt with the symptoms and signs of worms again in two parts, for worms outside the intestine and those within the gut. Those outside were said to cause local pain, fever, retention of urine and in the case of heart worms sudden deaths. Andry discussed the proposition that venereal diseases were caused by worms and admitted that such patients were often found to be infested, but of the causal relationship he was doubtful. Intestinal worms do, in fact, cause rather vague gastrointestinal upsets and these are fully described. The itching and tenesmus caused by threadworms, Andry's Ascarides, was well known.[30] A section of the book was devoted to the avoidance of infection by worms. Andry made the point that one cannot hope to avoid worms after death but can hope to do so during life. He considered that three factors predisposed to infection: bad air, bad food and overindulgence in food. Bad air and food contained numerous seeds of worms but certain foods in particular should be avoided . . . milk, sugary food, cider, melons and mushrooms but above all vinegar which was frequently full of worms and their seeds. The treatment of worms was dealt with, at length, a very large number of concoctions of the traditional pharmacy of his day being suggested as remedies. Before leaving Andry's important book it is worth considering the numerous other types of parasites he described and some of which he figured which are imaginary or else misinterpretations. This topic shows Andry at his weakest for he was particularly credulous in this respect. The literature of helminthology contains many fantastic descriptions of supposed parasites, a good example being one described by Benivieni, the " father of morbid anatomy ", at the end of the fifteenth century. He described a worm vomited by a patient as follows: " a worm quite four fingers long, rather fat, with smooth, round, red head no bigger than a pea and a forked tail shaped like the new moon, the rest of the body being hairy. It went on four feet, two joined together on the right side of its body and two on the left ".[31] Andry accepted worms at least as bizarre as this. He thought that worms changed their appearance with age so that they might come to resemble frogs, scorpions, birds and lizards. He classified these parasites according to the animals they resembled.[32] His volume of plates is particularly valuable in considering this aspect of the subject. It shows that these pseudo-helminths belong to three categories: those quite fantastic and impossible to account for, free living animals mistaken for parasites and true parasites in an unusual or degenerate state. The acceptance of these pseudo-helminths must have been due to two main causes, deliberate fraud on the part of patients purporting to have passed free living animals and the rudimentary state of zoological classification. Andry's book has been dealt with at this length because it gives a comprehensive account of human parasitology at the beginning of the eighteenth century, but a few years after the beginning of the scientific study of the subject. It thus forms a baseline from which the further development of the subject can be traced.

One of the most influential figures in eighteenth century parasitology was Peter Simon Pallas. He was not primarily a parasitologist but an explorer of the unknown parts of the Russian Empire. He was born in 1741 in Berlin, the son of the professor of surgery and after brilliant schooldays during which he mastered Latin, French and English and employed his leisure on natural history, he commenced his medical studies at the age of 15. He graduated M.D. at Leyden in 1760, his thesis entitled *De infestis viventibus intra-viventia* being his major contribution to parasitology. During his stay in Holland he saw excellent collections of natural objects which Dutch traders had accumulated from all over the world and this confirmed his taste for biology rather than the profession of medicine. In 1761 he spent a year in England, ostensibly to study medicine and surgery, but neglected these for zoology. His father endeavoured to make him practise his profession and for a short while he was an army surgeon but even then he occupied his time collecting materials for a *Description of the Insects in the March of Brandenburg*. He was elected F.R.S. in 1764 and in 1766 produced his most famous purely zoological work, the *Miscellanea zoologica*. In his goodly quarto of 200 pages he described a great variety of new species of animals including an African boar and a West Indian bat, but more than half the book is devoted to the study of molluscs. As Cuvier remarked he threw a sudden light " on those classes of the animal economy which were least known, and which had long been huddled together under the common appellation of worms ". Clarification of the classification of this group was clearly an important indirect contribution to parasitology. It is however to be regretted that Pallas did not continue his investigations in this field and left it with his views not properly matured.[33]

The purely parasitological section of the *Miscellanea zoologica* is an 18 page article on the bladder worms. He regarded all forms of these as a kind of tapeworm and he was first to suggest that the hydatid cysts found in man were of the same nature. He considered all bladder worms to belong to a single species, *Taenia hydatigena,* but he also drew attention to the similarity of the heads of the cystic worms of the mouse (*Cysticercus fasciolaris*) and the tapeworm of the cat (*Taenia crassicolis*). He believed that some individuals of the brood of *Taenia crassicollis* went astray in rodents, and degenerated into *Cysticercus fasciolaris*; but when their hosts were eaten by cats, and the worms thus transplanted to their fit soil, they cast off their degenerate joints, and returning to the normal form of *Taenia crassicollis,* became sexually mature.[34] One can but regret that an observer acute enough to have made that observation, so very near to the truth, did not concentrate his efforts on the study of parasites, for surely, the life-cycle of the tapeworm would have been worked out almost a hundred years earlier than in fact it was. Pallas was also alive to the possibilities of animal experiment in helminthology and at one time introduced tapeworm eggs into the abdominal cavity of a dog.

In 1767 Pallas was invited by Catherine II of Russia to fill the chair of natural history at Petersburg and for the next 42 years his life was spent exploring and studying the general natural history of Russia. It has been said that " a third of his life was spent in the desert, and the rest in his study ". He continued to make scattered observations on parasitology but his main work was to travel, and study the natural history of the extensive Russian Empire. He was a great favourite of the Empress Catherine who purchased his museum on terms very flattering to Pallas. She said that Russia could not be deprived of so fine a collection and asked Pallas to name a price. He suggested 15,000 roubles. " Mr. Pallas understands natural history much better than figures " replied the Empress, " he ought to have charged 20,000 roubles " and she paid him that sum and also allowed him to keep the museum for his life-time because " he so well understands how to make it most useful to mankind ". But despite royal favour his last years in Russia were not happy and he returned to his native land and died in 1811.

Several amateur naturalists have made important contributions to the study of helminthology but none were more valuable than those of Johan Göze, a German protestant pastor. This " indefatigable helminthologist ", as Leuckart called him, wrote what was by far the most comprehensive account of the parasites of man and animals to be published during the eighteenth century. His *Versuch einer Natur-*

geschichte der Eingeweidewürmer tierischer Körper was published in 1787 although the preface is dated from Quedlinburg in 1782. It was dedicated to Pallas and is a quarto of 466 pages with 35 pages of plates. His classification of parasites marked a great advance and resulted from his extremely extensive experience, for he dissected a wide variety of animals in a search for parasites. He divided parasites into eleven genera: *Ascaris, Trichocephalus, Gordius, Cucullanus, Strongylus, Pseudoechinorynchus, Planaria, Fasciola, Taenia,* and *Chaos* . . . the last being the Linnaean genus in which was lumped all the microscopic living organisms some of which were known at this time to lead parasitic lives.

The individual species of the parasites he described in considerable detail and grouped according to their hosts for man, other mammals, birds, fishes, and amphibians. The number of parasitic species described is considerable; thus 4 distinct species of tapeworm are described from man, 10 from other mammals, 14 from birds, 6 from fishes and 1 from other amphibians. Göze was the first to suggest that there were two species of common tapeworm in man besides the broad tapeworm and also, independently of Pallas recognized the similarity of the heads of *Cysticercus fasciolaris* and *Taenia crassicollis* but remarked " But why these two forms are so similar in the structures of their head, and yet so different in other respects . . . who can tell?".[35] Perhaps the most important discoveries of Göze were the scolex of *Coenurus cerebellis,* the highly pathogenic cystic worm of sheep, and of the scolex of the *Echinococcus* in hydatid cysts. It will be recalled that Pallas had postulated that hydatid cysts were of the same nature as the bladder worms. Göze believed in the zoological independence of the cystic worms and the tapeworms despite his observations on their similarities. He recognized this similarity by placing them in the same genus which he divided into two species, *Taenia visceralis* and *Taenia intestinalis.*

A powerful stimulus to the development of helminthology in general towards the end of the eighteenth century was given by the Academy of Science of Copenhagen which set as a prize essay, in 1780, the following subject, " Concerning the seeds of intestinal worms; whether tapeworms etc., are inborn in animals or enter from the outside ". We have already mentioned that Göze received a silver medal for his contribution on this topic but the gold medallist was M. Bloch, a doctor of medicine in Berlin. His prize-winning essay *Abhandlung von der Erzeugung der Eingeweidewürmer* was published in 1782 and translated into French in 1788. This work is divided into three main sections: a general introduction in which he comments on the importance of the study of parasitology from the point of view of medicine and the general neglect of this branch of natural history which is followed by a systematic classification and description of 42 species of parasites. The second part of it is devoted to the problem set by the Copenhagen Academy . . . the origin of intestinal worms. The last section is on treatment.

Bloch devised his own classification but it was, in its main divisions, very similar to that of Göze. He was however the first to draw attention to the presence or absence of hooklets on the tapeworm head as a specific character and he divided the genus *Taenia* into two groups " inarmartae " of which he described 16 species and " armartae " with 4 species. With regard to the general physiology of tapeworms he correctly regarded the segmental contents as ovaries and stated that the nourishment of the worm is absorbed through each individual segment. He described three species of bladder worms and comments that their origin is " un des plus grandes énigmes pour la naturaliste eclairer ". His opinion on the origin of intestinal worms, which has already been considered, of course coloured his ideas on prophylaxis and therapy. He held it to be impossible to destroy the seeds of the worms although appropriate measures might hinder their development and if already developed, expel them.

With the opening of the nineteenth century the production of texts of parasitology increased considerably. V. L. Brera, professor of medicine at Pavia, where Göze's fine collection of helminths was preserved, published some popular lectures on helminthology which were translated from the Italian into French in 1804. His views on the origin of parasites have already been considered and the three other lectures are devoted to classification, clinical manifestations and treatment. Each chapter is followed by an extensive annotated bibliography. In classification of tapeworms Brera followed Bloch in the use of hooklets as a key character but he still confounded the two common tapeworms,

Francesco Redi (1626-1697. (From an engraving in the Wellcome Collection.)

Pierre Simon Pallas (1741-1811). (From an engraving by F. G. Krüger.)

J. Steenstrup (1813-1897). (From Garboe (1961), *Geologiens Historie i Danmark,* Copenhagen: Reitzel.)

Joseph Leidy (1823-1891). (*Annals med. Hist.* 1923.)

PLATE IV

[*To face p. 16*

Karl Asmund Rudolphi (1771-1832). (From a lithograph by Schatt, after H. Löwenstein.)

David Gruby (1813-1873). (From Kisch, B. (1954): *Forgotten Leaders in Modern Medicine. Trans. Amer. Phil Soc. 44,* 193.)

C. Davaine. (From *L'oeuvre de C-J. Davaine* 1889.)

Thomas Spencer Cobbold (1826-1888).

PLATE V

To face p. 17]

T. solium and *T. saginata*. Brera, as a clinician, was impressed by the pathogenic effects of infestation by worms and criticized the idea held by helminthologists with a zoological point of view, such as Bloch, that they were for the most part harmless. He poured scorn on the idea that infestation by some worms was necessary for health. This idea is found in the parasitological writings of ancient China and even in those of Benjamin Rush.

By far the most important parasitological works of the early nineteenth century were those of C. A. Rudolphi who was one of the truly great biologists of his age and achieved a position of enormous authority during his lifetime, an authority which helped to delay the acceptance of some important truths. However, in the main, his work was of a very high order of excellence. He was born in 1771, in Sweden, of German parents. He studied medicine at Greifswald, becoming professor of anatomy there. Later, he went to Berlin where he remained until his death in 1832. He founded the Berlin Zoological Museum and was highly esteemed by his friends and pupils on account of his zeal for science and his noble, almost supersensitive temperament. He would, for example, never perform experiments on animals and once said that the prospect of world-wide fame would not induce him to be as callous as Brunner who had made some experiments involving the extirpation of the pancreas from living dogs. His main contributions to biology were in comparative anatomy, physiology and parasitology. In a collection of short essays Rudolphi recorded a number of valuable observations in comparative anatomy of which his microscopical studies of the intestinal villi of different vertebrates are of special interest for their own sake and as an example of the early use of the microscope in histology. In physiology he did important work writing in his old age his *Grundriss der Physiologie* which was unfinished at his death. In this book Rudolphi repudiated many of the extravagant ideas on the essence of life current at that time and emphasized the importance of chemical processes in vital functions. The chapter on human anatomy is one of the most brilliant parts of the work, representing a considerable advance on the work of Bichat. The whole work illustrates the vast strides that had been made in physiology during the early decades of the nineteenth century.[36]

His parasitological work is represented by his *Entozoorum sive vermium intestinalium historia naturalis* published in two volumes in 1808 and 1810 and his *Entozoorum synopsis cui accedunt mantissa duplex et indices locupletissima* of 1819. As a result of these works the number of known species of parasites was trebled. In his *Synopsis* he lists a total of 993 species dividing them into two groups, distinct and dubious, but even the distinct species amount to 552. He records 146 species of Taenia although 53 are dubious. These works are of an extremely scholarly nature. The first volume of the *Entozoorum sive vermium intestinalium historia naturalis* opens with a 172 page bibliography containing 629 references. The remainder of the volume is occupied by a general account of parasitology under the title of *Physiologia entozoologia* and a section on their clinical and pathological effects under the title of *Entozoologia pracitica*. The second volume consists of systematic descriptions of all known species and runs to 457 pages. His *Synopsis* is on a somewhat different plan but again is a monumental work of over 800 pages characterized by the same exhaustive thoroughness. Parasites are divided into the following natural orders, *Nematoides, Acanthocephala, Trematoda, Cestoidea, Cystica* and *Entozoa dubia*. Each order is characterized, then the characters of each genus are given, followed by a brief description of each species with references to the original literature and a note of their habitat. This section is, however but a 200 page summary and a much fuller description of each species is given in the main part of the work entitled *Mantissa entozoologia*. There is a relatively brief account of the general anatomy and physiology of parasites and a fine annotated bibliography. There is also a useful zoologically classified index of all species of animals showing which parasites infest them with their internal habitat indicated by a code letter. The least satisfactory part of the book is the three plates which are rather small and of little use. With the publication of such works it is not surprising that Rudolphi was regarded as the foremost parasitologist of his day. There had certainly never been before nor has there been since such a comprehensive account of the whole subject and the student of the day must have felt there was no need for him to go further than to consult the works of

Rudolphi. It has with justice been said that the works of Rudolphi did for parasitology what the works of Linnaeus did for zoology.[37]

Despite the almost definitive character of the writings of Rudolphi the flow of parasitological texts did not immediately dry up. J. S. Olombel, ex-médecin en chef in the army of Napoleon and professor of medicine, published his short *Remarques sur les maladies vermineuses* in 1816. This was essentially a book for practising doctors rather than zoologists, giving a simple classification of human parasites with brief descriptions. The bulk of the book was devoted to the origin of parasites, prophylactic measures, clinical manifestations and treatment. Similarly, the much more elaborate *Uber lebende Würmer in lebenden Menschen* published by J. G. Bremser in 1819 was designed as a book for practitioners. Bremser was an eminent helminthologist and custodian of the Imperial Museum in Vienna, to whom Rudolphi dedicated his *Synopsis*. Bremser's book is a handsome quarto containing some of the earliest and best coloured plates of parasites.

Of parasitological literature in English there was at this period virtually nothing. Various textbooks devoted short passages to the subject, none more clear and succinct than that in Matthew Baillie's *Morbid Anatomy of Some of the Most Important Parts of the Human Body,* first published in 1793. He noted that tapeworm infections were very uncommon in Britain and with regard to the origin of intestinal worms, although clearly in doubt about it, wrote " I own, that the grounds for believing that in some orders of animals equivocal generation takes place, appear stronger than those for a contrary opinion ".[38] Throughout the first half of the nineteenth century there were only case reports and a few review articles and lectures on the *Entozoa* in English although in 1827 there was an American translation of Brera's book. In the 1840's the Ray Society, in its annual reports, published several translations of continental works on helminthology usually by George Busk. It was not, however, until the Sydenham Society, in 1857, published two volumes containing translations of Kuchenmeister's *Manual of Animal and Vegetable Parasites* and von Siebold's *Tape and Cystic Worms* that an adequate systematic treatise on parasitology became available in English.

In 1845, however, the Ray Society did publish a translation of a book which although not primarily a parasitological text was in fact, probably the most important single contribution to the science of helminthology in the first half of the nineteenth century. The work referred to is *On Alternation of Generations; or the Propagation and Development of Animals through Alternate Generations* by J. J. S. Steenstrup, a Danish naturalist. Steenstrup was born in 1813 in North Jutland, the son of a clergyman and studied geology and zoology at the University of Copenhagen. He was an extraordinarily gifted and many-sided investigator. His first important treatise was his now classical palaeobotanical work on the peat bogs in North Zeeland, published in 1837. In 1839 and 1840 he travelled in Iceland mainly for the purpose of geological research but at the same time indulged his interest in marine zoology. He studied the development of the jellyfish, and it was these investigations which started in his mind the train of thought that led to the publication of his treatise on alternation of generations in 1842. In 1845 he was made professor of zoology at Copenhagen and returned to his zoological and archaeological studies, discovering the Stone Age shell mounds (refuse heaps) which he studied with valuable zoological and ethnographical results and opened up a wide area for research.[39]

But important as his other researches were his short treatise on alternation of generations, one of the most illuminating generalizations in the history of biology, is of prime interest in the history of parasitology and must now be considered in some detail.

There were already published observations suggesting that some animals were not developed directly from parents like themselves. A. von Camisso in 1819 had noted that certain marine ascidians (*Salpae*) occurred either in chains or as individuals and that the individuals contained chains of embryos whereas the chains of salpae contained individual embryos. He therefore concluded that there was an alternation of generation between the two forms. Moreover, the Norwegian naturalist M. Sars in a series of papers published between 1828 and 1841, had gradually unravelled the life cycle of the common jellyfish showing that the animal alternated between a fixed polypoid stage and a free living medusa. His work was confirmed independently by von Siebold at Danzig. Steenstrup himself, whilst in Iceland, had made observations showing that the anatomy of the polypoid animals was very similar to that of the medusa. These observations, he remarked, "present highly remarkable phenomena, which may be truly called peculiar, although they are not fundamentally isolated".[40] He then goes on to describe the development of another group of animals, the Claviform polyps. The information on this group was much less complete and he had to rely considerably on his own observations. "What I have been able to collect in this instance, will probably be regarded with respect to the object I have in view, as very little. I think, however, that even in this little, as in the sketch of a picture not yet filled up, what the whole probably may be, will be not indistinctly discerned".[41] Whilst in Iceland Steenstrup had seen medusa-like individuals bud off from the polyps and swim away and in water taken from near the surface there were very similar creatures except that they were larger and contained a new lobate organ which "I can only look upon it as connected with generation". He goes on "upon reviewing this sketch it can hardly be considered to present an instance of metamorphosis, since it is not the same individuals which in the course of time exhibit various forms, but we see here also, a series of generation whose succession in definite order is necessary to the complete development of the species".[42]

In the fourth chapter he turns to the subject of parasites. It was well known that thousands of small animalcules known as cercariae were sometimes found in the water in which the common fresh water molluscs *Planorbis cornea* and *Limnaeus stagnalis* were kept. It had also been noticed that the bodies of the cercariae bore a close resemblance to parasitic flukes of the genus then known as *Distoma*. The cercariae, however, unlike the flukes had a long tail and were actively motile. It was known that these cercariae settled down and became encysted, sometimes on the snails and sometimes on other objects. This was the sum of knowledge relating to those creatures until Steenstrup began investigation of them about 1840. As von Siebold had written "what becomes of the pupa cercariae is at present an enigma".[43] Steenstrup showed that these cercariae remained encysted for several months but if opened after a period had the exact form of *Distoma* and these *Distoma* he found beneath the skin and in the liver of some specimens of *Limnaeus stagnalis* in August 1841. A few months later he observed freshly liberated flukes about to penetrate the body of a snail. The next question to be answered was " whence comes the free-swimming cercariae?" The answer was to be found in the writings of Bojanus who had shown that they were liberated from what he called the " king's yellow worm " which was found under the capsules of the snails' viscera. The interior of these worms could be seen under the microscope, to be filled with small cercariae. The origin of the king's yellow worm was however still a mystery. Steenstrup examined thousands of these worms, tracing them back to their smallest form, and from their anatomy it was plain that they were not derived from either cercariae or flukes. Then he noticed that some snails harboured " only entozoa, which had the outward form of the nurses (Steenstrup's name for the king's yellow worm) but which contained progeny consisting of actual " nurses " . . . Therefore, he wrote, " I consequently cannot doubt but that it is normal for the ' nurses ' to originate in creatures of similar appearance ".[44] He continues " We have then followed the *Distoma* to its third stage of ascent, and I have not been able to detect any more generations; and am, consequently, not in a condition at present to trace the origin of the *Distoma* further back. I entertain, however, the not unfounded supposition, that the parent ' nurses ' do not arise from other similar creatures, but that they proceed originally from ova; for as is stated above, it must be assumed that the full-grown fluke, like all the other species of this genus or family is oviparous ".[45] Moreover, the ova and embryos of a related *Trematode* genus, the *Monostoma*, parasites in water birds, were known, and their embryos developed a striking resemblance to *Distoma* " parent nurses ". He therefore thought it unlikely that they developed directly into adult *Monostoma*. " If we now introduce a link such as we have presented to us by the *Monostoma* into the series of development of the *Distoma* given above, the whole cycle will be completed . . . ".[46]

Thus Steenstrup, drawing together the scattered observations of others, supplementing them with the results of his own careful observations, brilliantly elucidated the life cycle of one species of liver fluke which illustrates so perfectly his ideas of the alternation of generations.

With regard to other parasitic species he remarked, " That all trematode animals are developed in this way, that all are obliged to undergo such alternation of generation cannot be directly affirmed from the facts adduced; these, however, are sufficient to warrant the supposition that this is probably the case ".[47] In other families of entozoa he thought that an alternation of generation was very probable although in some groups there was no evidence of it. " The cystic entozoa on the contrary, betray in many ways that they are a nursing ' generation ' . . . Probably the full grown animal of this division is quite unknown . . . ".[48] This last remark strikes one as a little odd for the resemblance of the heads of cystic and tapeworms had been known for many years. It probably only indicates that, despite his brilliant contribution to the subject, Steenstrup was no parasitologist; indeed his work involved but a short interlude in a long and productive life.

Another important parasitologist of the early nineteenth century was Félix Dujardin, who was born in 1801, the son of a watchmaker. He was naturally gifted with a very versatile talent and early in life became a very skilled worker with his hands. He did not turn finally to the study of zoology until he was over 30 years of age, before then being an engineer, a bookseller, a professor of geometry and chemistry and a professor of geology. In 1840 he was appointed professor of zoology at Rennes and there he remained until his death in 1860. Like so many parasitologists he was a naturalist with wide interests and made valuable contributions in other areas of science. He made technical improvements in microscope illumination employing a system of lenses beneath the stage of the microscope, the ancestor of the modern condensor. He was the first to observe the motility of the leucocytes, to prove that sponges were animals and, in a great work, published in 1841, to bring some order to the heterogeneous group of microscopic animals and plants known loosely as *Infusoria.* His parasitological work seems to have been done between the years 1837 and 1851. He was the earliest worker to appreciate that *Trematodes* and *Cestodes* pass part of their lives in an intermediate host and recognized that the bladder worms were part of the life cycle of the tapeworms, but curiously, did not publish his ideas, a fact, which in later life he bitterly regretted. In 1838 he discovered the first parasitic species of Rotifer which he named *Albertia* in honour of his son. Dujardin was a pioneer in the study of the parasites of invertebrates, publishing in 1842 a memoir on the nematode parasites of insects. In the following year he published an important memoir on the helminths infesting shrews. In this work he established that a certain *Distoma* was acquired by the shrews eating slugs infested with the intermediate form of the parasites. He also introduced the term "proglottis" to describe a segment of tapeworm. His main work in parasitology was, however, his *Histoire naturelle des helminthes ou vers intestinaux* published in 1845. This excellent book of over 600 pages gives detailed descriptions of some hundreds of parasites and was the fruit of some 10 years' intensive study of parasites during which time he had personally dissected 2,400 vertebrates and 300 invertebrates specially to search for parasites. He proposed a novel classification of helminths based on whether or not they were hermaphrodites and whether or not they possessed an intestinal tract but the main value of the work lies in its excellent, detailed zoological descriptions which include many new species.[49]

Yet another famous French parasitologist was Casimir Davaine who was born in northern France in 1812. He is one of those figures in the history of science who have been most undeservedly forgotten. When he is remembered it is for his work on anthrax although the extent of his contribution and its priority in point of time is seldom appreciated and the bulk of the credit for our knowledge of this disease is given to Koch and Pasteur. However, Davaine's work on anthrax forms but a small part, important though it is, of his great contribution to biology. The neglect from which Davaine has suffered perhaps stems from the fact that he himself was of a modest disposition and that he was all his life a general practitioner of medicine never holding any academic position nor even having a proper laboratory. As a medical practitioner he was however successful and included amongst his patients such people as Claude Bernard and Baron Rothschild. Despite his age he served as an army doctor in the Franco-Prussian War during which time he wrote a short treatise giving his philosophy of life entitled *Les éléments du Bonheur*. Although we are chiefly concerned with his parasitological writings, it will be of interest to give a summary of his other main contributions to science. These included an impor-

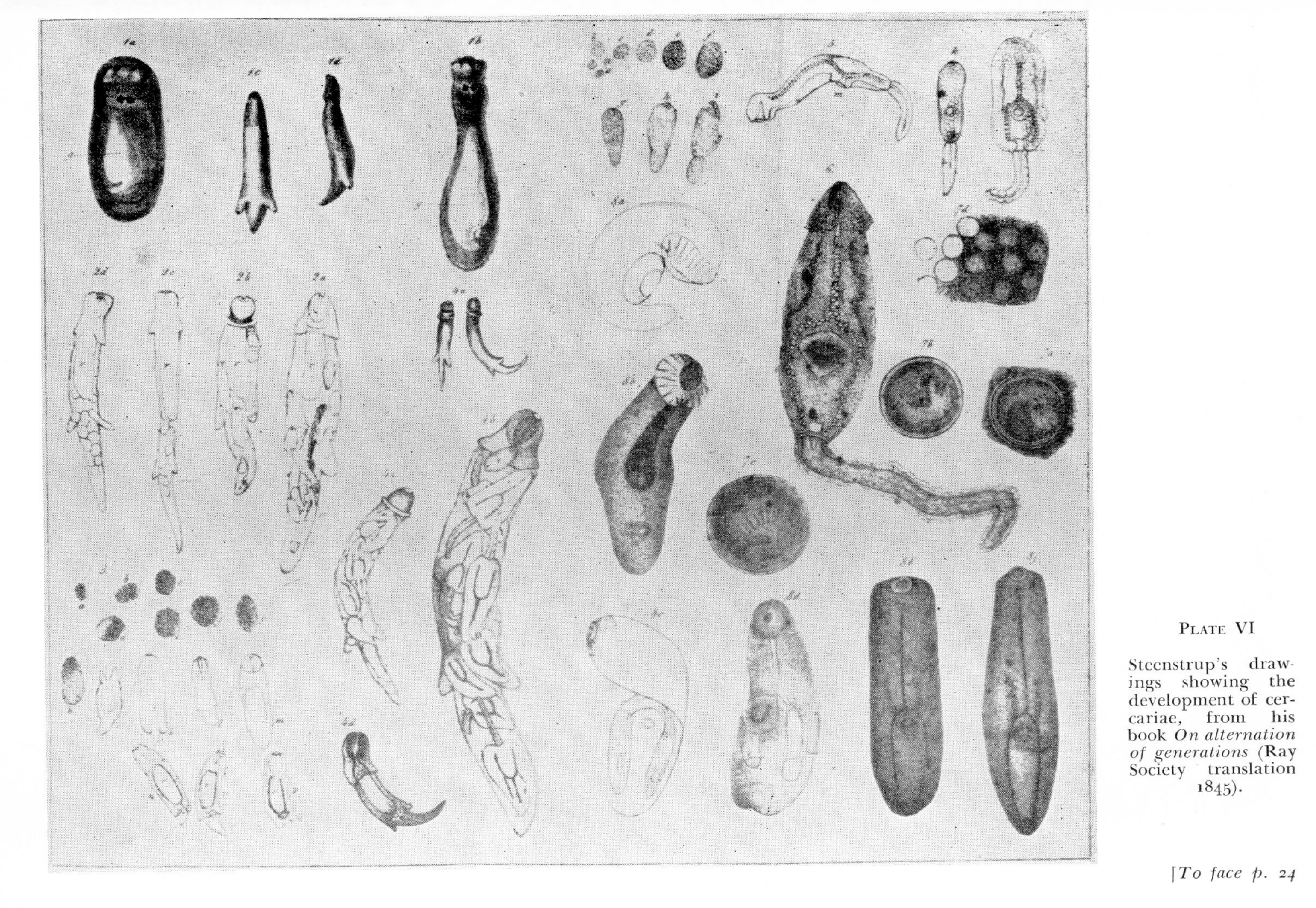

PLATE VI

Steenstrup's drawings showing the development of cercariae, from his book *On alternation of generations* (Ray Society translation 1845).

[To face p. 24

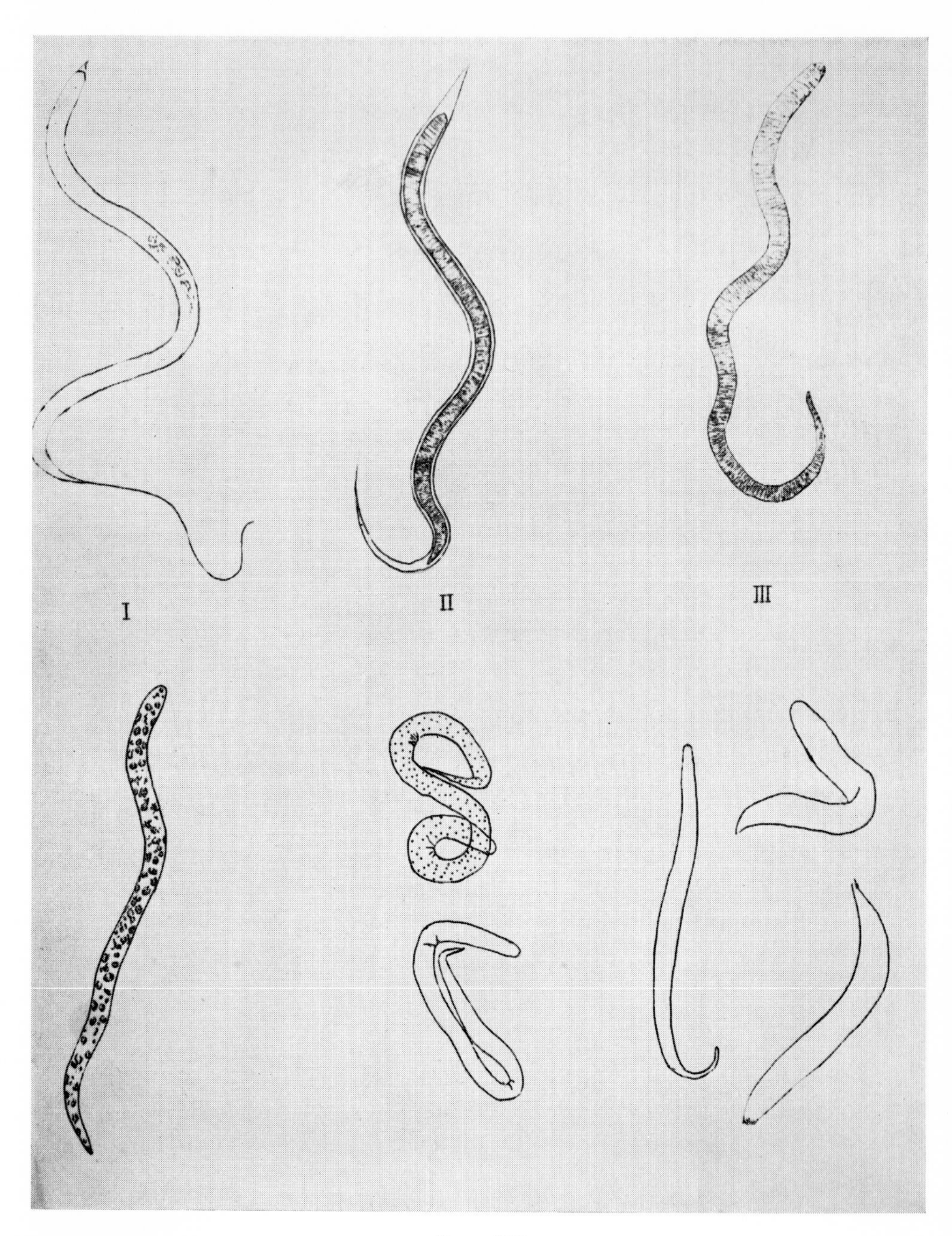

PLATE VII

Manson's drawings of embryo filaria (from the Custom's Reports, 1877).

To face p. 25]

tant memoir on the development of oysters, a comprehensive review of the science of teratology as well as studies on the movement of leucocytes, which he compared with amoebae, and investigations of the various species of animals, such as certain *Rotifers, Nematodes* and *Infusoria* which can withstand prolonged periods of desiccation.

His original parasitological observations include the description of two new species of human parasites, an intestinal flagellate, *Pentatrichomonas hominis* and a rare cestode, *Inermicapsifer madagascariensis.* He showed the value of microscopical examination of faeces in the diagnosis of helminthiasis, being the first to do so (1857), and showed that the eggs of *Ascaris* remain infective for long periods in a damp environment. His parasitological studies were not confined to the animal kingdom; he also investigated the eelworm of wheat as well as various fungus diseases of plants.[50] Undoubtedly his main contribution to parasitology was, however, his *Traité des entozoaires et des maladies vermineuses de l'homme et des animaux domestiques* published in 1860. The book opens with a synopsis of parasites classified zoologically into six groups, *Protozoaires, Cestoides, Trématodes, Acanthocéphales, Nématoides* and *Acanthothéques.* The subdivision of the group *Protozoaires* shows that some progress had been made with the Linnaean order *Chaos.* They are divided into three groups: *Vibrions, Trichomonas* and *Paramecium.* The descriptions of the species are brief but clear and there are excellent illustrations in the text. The main body of the book consists of descriptions of parasites classified anatomically according to their site of infection in man and in animals. This part of the work gives little detail of the anatomy of the individual parasite but gives a very full account of their natural history, geographical distribution and symptomatology. Many clinical cases are reported in full. The bibliography lists over 1,300 authors and the whole work gives a very full account of the state of parasitology in the middle of the nineteenth century.

Up to the 1860's parasitology had been almost completely neglected in Great Britain, neither important original observations nor significant contribution to the literature having emanated from these islands. The first Briton to achieve a distinguished position in the science of parasitology was T. S. Cobbold who was during his lifetime the chief

British authority on the subject. Cobbold was born in 1828, the son of a well-to-do country clergyman. After serving an apprenticeship with J. G. Crosse, the well-known Norwich surgeon, he proceeded to Edinburgh University where he graduated in 1851. After a few months of postgraduate study in Paris he returned to Edinburgh and worked in the department of anatomy under John Goodsir. Not being dependent upon his profession for his daily bread, he resolved not to practise medicine but to devote himself to a career in biology. Cobbold's main work in Goodsir's department lay in the field of comparative anatomy and his interest in parasitology almost certainly arose as a result of observing numerous parasites in the various animals which he dissected. The literature on parasites in English was scanty and he soon started to scan the Continental journals for new facts on what was becoming his favourite subject. In 1854 he made his first parasitological discovery whilst dissecting a giraffe. In the bile ducts he found numerous specimens of a species of *Fasciola* which were however much larger than the well known *Fasciola hepatica* of sheep. He named the new species *Fasciola giganta* and must have been very proud of his discovery for 10 years later he used a coloured drawing of this parasite as the frontispiece to his great book on the entozoa.

In 1857 he decided to seek fame, if not fortune, in London and obtained the post of lecturer in botany at St. Mary's Hospital. In 1861 he was made also a lecturer at the Middlesex Hospital. Cobbold, however, never obtained a post of the first rank in London although in 1872 he became a professor of botany and helminthology at the Royal Veterinary College. On his arrival in London he continued in his resolve not to undertake any clinical work so that he might spend his whole time on scientific work. He obtained permission to dissect animals dying in the Zoological Society's garden and in the four years 1857-1860 examined 122 such animals in the search for parasites. This source, together with contributions from farmers, the market and sporting friends, soon provided him with a great practical experience of parasitology. Meanwhile his practical experience was supplemented by extensive reading. He ransacked the libraries of London in search of literature and with the aid of Continental correspondents, who included some of the most eminent parasitologists, he was able to build up a tolerably complete collection of the foreign literature. In the summer of 1864 he was elected to the Fellowship of the Royal Society and with the publication in the autumn of the same year of his fine book *Entozoa, an Introduction to the Study of Helminthology* his reputation as a parasitologist equal to the greatest on the Continent, and the first in Great Britain and her growing tropical empire, was established. The book was received enthusiastically: "a noble contribution to the literature of the subject"; "a credit to our national literature"; "a fresh starting place"; "enables the students of helminthology to comprehend the precise position which that science now occupies", were some of the comments of reviewers. All were unanimous on the elegant standard of production, "emphatically what our friends across the channel would call an édition de luxe. Printed on the finest paper and adorned with numerous and very beautiful illustrations, it is perhaps the handsomest work on a medical subject with which we are acquainted". One minor criticism there was and that was of the meagreness of the clinical descriptions, which was excused on the grounds that the author was not a practising physician.

The book contained an excellent account of general parasitology and then gave a detailed account of all the parasites of man. The work was rounded off with a fine bibliography, extending to 60 pages, of all the important articles on internal parasites that had appeared in English during the previous 50 years. His aim was to do for British and American authors what Davaine had done for the Continental writers, and Cobbold considered that taken together their works "present as complete a résumé of entozoological literature as anyone could reasonably desire or hope to obtain". The success of his book encouraged Cobbold to set up in practice as a physician specializing in parasitic diseases and many interesting patients and pathological material from all over the world were referred to him. As he wrote, "through the kindness of correspondents and contributors of specimens from abroad, I am constantly put in possession of novel facts in helminthology". Thus on the 7th March, 1878, at a meeting of the Linnean Society, Cobbold presented, on Patrick Manson's behalf, the latter's remarkable discovery of the development of embryo filaria in the body of a mosquito. Cobbold continued active in parasitological work almost until his death. In 1879 he published a new textbook, *Parasites; a Treatise on the Entozoa of Man and Animals Including Some Account of the Ectozoa.* This was not a new edition of his earlier book but an entirely new work with a far wider design. In addition to describing the parasites of man he gave a full account of the known parasites of the lower animals. This part of the book, he hoped, would enable naturalists to identify any parasites they came across in the course of their dissections and was in some measure an act of self-defence, for hundreds of correspondents were constantly seeking his help in the identification of their " finds ". This work was intended to " place a reasonable limit on the number of future applicants ". In 1885 Cobbold's health began to fail and when he died it was said of him that it was " not too much to affirm that his peculiar place in the profession can hardly be filled up ".[51]

Having thus traced the general development of parasitology from ancient times until the middle of the nineteenth century, by which time it had become a well established branch of science, the history of the subject will be illustrated by the consideration of the growth of our knowledge of certain particular parasites. The particular parasites have been chosen because their histories illustrate distinct steps in the history of parasitology as a whole.

Chapter II

THE CESTODES

THE best-known cestodes of man, as we now know, exist as two different distinct parasitic forms each involving different host species. There is the adult tapeworm which lives in the intestinal tract of its host and the larval, cystic stage which is found in such organs as the liver, brain and subcutaneous tissues. It was not until the middle of the nineteenth century that it was finally shown that these two parasitic forms were but different stages in the life cycle of a single species. The early history of our knowledge of these two, apparently distinct parasites is therefore unconnected and may conveniently be considered separately. We have already shown that ancient civilized man and even primitive man were aware of the existence of both the adult worm and the cystic larva. The history of our knowledge of the nature of the adult tapeworm will be considered first.

History of the Tapeworm

A number of questions must have occurred to anyone reflecting on the natural history of tapeworms: what was the nature of the thing? was it indeed an animal? whence did it come? how was it constructed? how did it feed, breathe, grow and reproduce? A clear understanding of these points required the cumulative studies of many investigators over many centuries.

The animal nature of tapeworms was appreciated by doctors of the ancient world such as Hippocrates, Aristotle and Galen. Paulus Aegineta considered that they were "a conversion of the membrane which lines the inside of the intestine into a living body".[52] We have already noted that he was familiar with the most characteristic symptom of infestation, the passage of segments of the worm in the faeces. The Arabs introduced the notion that these segments of tapeworms were a separate species of parasite, the Chabb-al-kari or vermes cucurbitini, a belief which persisted until the eighteenth century. They also postulated that a tapeworm might be a compound animal made up by the joining of the cucurbitini.[53] Mention of the cucurbitini brings up the question of the number of the species of tapeworms, particularly those parasitizing man. Aristotle was familiar with the tapeworms of man and several of his domestic animals but whether or not man harboured more than one kind of worm, he did not know. Indeed the possibility was not raised until the Arabs attempted to separate the cucurbitini from the true tapeworms. Modern knowledge of the natural history of tapeworms, the feeding habits of the peoples living around the Mediterranean Sea and such descriptions of tapeworms as we have from ancient times make it virtually certain that the common cestode must have been *Taenia saginata,* the beef tapeworm. Religious prohibitions on the consumption of pork amongst the Arabs and Jews must have shielded them at least, from infestation by *Taenia solium.* However, we know that the ancient Greeks were familiar with cysticercus cellulosae, the larval form of *T. solium,* in the pig and so presumably some of the tapeworms infesting them must have been of this species. There is however no reason to believe that the ancient inhabitants of the Mediterranean basin were troubled with the third main human species of tapeworm, *Diphyllobothrium latum.* Thus the total experience of the ancient writers was probably confined to *T. saginata* and *T. solium,* the former predominating, but the two species were not distinguished.

Two Swiss physicians, Thadeus Dunus and Felix Platter of Basle first drew attention to the existence of the broad tapeworm *Diphyllobothrium latum.* Platter in his *Opus praxeos medicae* published in 1602 clearly distinguished two species of human tapeworm which from then on were known as the " Species prima et secunda Platteri ".[54] At this time the head of the tapeworm had not been described but the distinction between the genera *Taenia* and *Diphyllobothrium* could be made fairly readily from the appearance of the segments which were much shorter and broader in *Diphyllobothrium,* the genital pore of which was placed medially rather than laterally. This genital pore, was, of course not recognized as such for many years. Andry described it as a " spine ", but it nonetheless served as a distinguishing feature. The distinction between the segments of *T. saginata* and *T. solium* is much less obvious and went quite unsuspected until late in the eighteenth century. That there was some variation between individual tapeworms other than *Diphyllobothrium* was to some extent appreciated, and even illustrated, but the differences were not sufficiently striking to suggest a specific difference. Moreover, it was held, for example by Pallas, that tapeworms differed in character according to their host species and even between different hosts of the same species and he noted that "from reasons which do not seem exactly to harmonize with the apparent constitution of the host, and which are difficult to explain, it is sometimes delicate, thin and slender, and at other times very large, thick and as it were flattened". This description almost certainly applies to the two species *T. solium* and *T. saginata* although Pallas did not appreciate this.

The characters of the head of the tapeworm as specific features were not appreciated until the late eighteenth century and indeed most early writers considered the broad end of the tapeworm to be the head. Edward Tyson corrected this error in his detailed description of tapeworms published in 1683. He appreciated that the head was at the narrow end, although he did not actually see the head of the specimen of *T. saginata*, which he obtained from a young man who "dragged it from himself, not without some frightful apprehensions, that guts, and all were coming out; he plainly perceived it alive, and to move; and having put it into a wide-mouthed glass, it often endeavoured by raising its body to get out". Tyson did however see the head of a tapeworm taken from a dog "observing here their heads hispid, or thick beset with hairs or small spikes".[55]

The following year Redi illustrated tapeworms from both cats and dogs. The drawings are on a small scale and rather crude but suggest the appearance of suctorial pits rather than hooklets. Andry (1718) was the first to illustrate a human tapeworm showing the scolex, again on rather a small scale, but showing unmistakably the four suctorial pits but no hooklets of *T. saginata*. The head of *Diphyllobothrium* had meanwhile not been described and in 1750 the situation was confused by Bonnet who described a human tapeworm in which the head is evidently that of *T. saginata* and the body that of *Diphyllobothrium*.

It is curious that the existence of this worm with a head showing four suctorial pits, broad segments and median genital pore, went unchallenged by all the helminthological writers even into the nineteenth century; although they never could, from their own experience, have confirmed the existence of such a creature.[56] Moreover, Bonnet himself, in 1777, corrected his own error by describing, for the first time, the true head of *Diphyllobothrium* with its attenuated outline and suctorial grooves. Charles Bonnet was born at Geneva in 1720, the son of wealthy parents of Huguenot descent. He was a lawyer and town councillor who studied biology as a hobby. He made a number of important discoveries of which his demonstration of parthenogenesis in aphids is the most noteworthy. In later life he suffered from some ocular disease which compelled him to give up practical observation and devote himself to speculative works. In this field too he was most influential although his preformation theory and views on evolution have been superseded.[57]

Linnaeus only added to the confusion by describing in 1762, a species which he called *T. vulgaris* with two genital pores on each segment which was probably only an abnormal form of either *T. saginata* or *T. solium*. Göze was the first to distinguish two human species of *Taenia,* " the familiar large one, with long, thick, flattened joints " and a thinner and more delicate type which he named *T. cucurbitini grandis saginata* and *T. cucurbitina plana pellucida* respectively. However, he failed to recognize that the species had differently constructed scolices and in fact ascribed a head with a circle of hooklets to both species.[58] For many years there was a failure to correlate the absence or presence of hooklets with stouter and more delicate segments respectively. Indeed some people, such as F. S. Leuckart, uncle of the more famous R. Leuckart, were of the opinion that tapeworms lost their hooklets with age just as a man loses his hair. Yet others considered the armed and unarmed species as mere varieties, if not related to different hosts, related to geographical distributions. This view was to some extent borne out by what was probably a genuine difference in distribution of the two species on the continent of Europe. For whereas Rudolphi, in Berlin, found the armed *T. solium* to be the commonest human tapeworm, the very competent helminthologist Bremser, in Vienna, saw only the unarmed *T. saginata* and, in fact, had only ever seen hooklets on the heads of worms sent to him by Rudolphi.[59] It was not until 1853 that Kuchenmeister clearly distinguished two human species of *Taenia* with differing scolices, external measurements of segments and uterine branches. He proposed calling the worm without hooklets *T. mediocanallata* and under such a name it was known for a number of years. However, R. Leuckart drew attention to the earlier, incomplete differentiation of the two species by Göze and re-introduced part of his terminology altering *T. mediocanallata* to *T. saginata*.[60] Even at this date the distinction between the two species was not universally accepted and the matter was not placed beyond doubt until the whole life cycle of the tapeworm had been worked out and Leuckart showed that *T. saginata* was related to the cysticercal stage in the cow, not the pig.

The first person to make any detailed studies of the anatomy and physiology of adult tapeworms was Edward Tyson whose observations were published in the *Philosophical Transactions of the Royal Society* for 1683. Tyson was born in 1650 in Somerset and although educated mainly at Oxford took the M.D. degree of Cambridge and settled in London. He was physician to Bridewell and Bethlehem hospitals but his scientific work lay in the field of anatomy, particularly comparative anatomy. He was author of works on the anatomy of the porpoise, opossum, shark and polecat besides his parasitological works. His most famous work was on the " Orang Outang, sive Homo sylvestris or the anatomy of a Pygmy ", actually an African chimpanzee, not a true orang outang. In this work his dissection is carefully described and is followed by a learned essay on the pygmies of the ancients. Tyson was a man of considerable learning and a keen book collector. As such he is satirized by Garth in the *Dispensary*.

> " When for advice the vulgar throng, he's found
> with number of vile books, besieged around.
>
> Here dregs and sediments of auctions reign,
> refuse of fairs and gleanings of Duck lane;
> And up these walls much Gothic lumber climbs,
> with Swiss philosophy and Runick rhymes;".[61]

Tyson's paper on the tapeworm, *Lumbricus latus,* he called it, occupies 31 pages of the *Philosophical Transactions*. His account is based mainly on the worms of man and the dog but he was aware that tapeworms occurred widely in nature and were particularly frequent in fishes " as in Pikes, Whitings, Bleaks, Crabs, Herrings, etc ". He described the external features of the worms in great detail, noted the variation in size of the segments in different parts of the worm and corrected the prevalent view that the broad end was the head. He also noted " That likewise there is a great difference of these joints in the various species of this worm (for I think there are more sorts than one)". He discussed the possible length of tapeworm quoting one report of a patient who, during one year, passed a total of 800 feet of tapeworm. This length he thought might have come from several worms but one of his own patients passed at one time a length of 24 feet with 507 segments. Tyson was particularly interested in two anatomical features of tapeworm; the little protuberances found on each segment which we now know as the genital pore and the head. He noted the constant occurrence of these tubercles on segments and the fact that they surrounded an orifice " which would easily enough admit of a hog's bristle ". He described them as occurring " much about the middle of the joints, on the edges; most frequently alternately, in one joint on the right hand, in the other on the left; sometimes two, seldom more, on the same side ". It is interesting that he must have been familiar with *Diphyllobothrium* also, for he described the tapeworms as of two sorts, in the other " these protuberances are placed about the middle of the flat of the worm ". With regard to their function, he considered the orifices to be mouths because the animal apparently had no other mouth. The orifices he found full of a fluid which he took to be chyle. He discussed the possibility that they were the openings of a tracheal system such as is found in insects but dismissed the idea because " the chyle must slip into them, and so spoil them from being lungs ".

With regard to the head he remarked " The head of this worm is obscure, and has created many controversies amongst the curious anatomists; who yet have been forced to confess, after observing vast quantities of this worm, that they are still at a loss, and know nothing certain of it. But what I have observed of the head of this worm, in three several ones I have taken out of the bodies of dogs upon dissection, where I know I have the whole makes me to be something more at a certainty ". Having found one in the small intestine he traced it up from the free, broad end towards the narrow end which he found in the duodenum and " did so firmly stick, and had fastened itself to the inward coat of the intestine, that it was not without some trouble, by gently raising it with my nail, that I freed it from its adhesion ". The worm was in active motion, contracting and expanding its segments and " it happening to fall off my finger, it presently took hold again, and gave me much trouble to free a second time from its adhesion, as at the first ". He put the worm into " spirit of wine that I might the more carefully view it with a microscope at home ". Here he discovered that the head was " thick beset with two orders of spikes or hooks " and could not, " with extraordinary glasses too, inform myself of any orifice here, which we may suppose to be the mouth ". He noted that the head end was not perfectly flat but a " little globus ".

Finally Tyson reflected on the nature of the tapeworm, writing, " Upon the whole, I have been some times apt to think, what analogy there may be between this jointed worm and knotted plants; of which each joint can so easily propagate itself. And whether it may not be thought an animal, Plant animal or Zoophyton, bred in animals' bodies; since so large and frequent detruncations of the body does not destroy the life of the whole; which I think can scarce be instanced in any animal besides ".[62]

It is strange that Tyson does not appear to have examined microscopically the fluid exuded from the papillary orifices, and which he took for chyle. He would then have seen the eggs of the tapeworm and surely revised his opinion as to their function. A few years later *Taenia* eggs were described by Andry but he did not appreciate that they were extruded from the orifices in question.[63]

Not until the late eighteenth century was it appreciated that the segmental contents were largely ovaries, as stated by Bloch. Even Göze, who knew that the papillary openings communicated with the ovaries, nonetheless thought that they also absorbed some nourishment, particularly in the lower segments of the worm.[64] No further details of the anatomy of tapeworms were discovered until well into the nineteenth century and a full understanding of their anatomy awaited the use of the techniques of embedding, sectioning and staining which were introduced into helminthology by Leuckart about 1860. The detailed anatomy of the sexual apparatus of the segments was gradually pieced together by the work of a number of German scientists such as Mehlis, Platner and von Siebold and the first full analysis of the generative apparatus was given by R. Leuckart in the first edition of his *Parasites of Man* published in 1862.[65]

The History of the Cystic Worms

Having considered the development of our knowledge of the adult tapeworm it will be convenient to trace the history of our knowledge of the bladder or cystic worms whose connection with the tapeworms was first suspected as recently as 150 years ago. The cystic stage in the life history of the tapeworm must have been noticed by primitive man in animals killed for food or for sacrificial purposes. Kuchenmeister has suggested that the Mosaic prohibition of the flesh of the pig, hare and rabbit was probably because of their being known to harbour cysticerci.[66] Aristotle in his *Historia animalium* speaks of the cysticerci of pigs as having been known for ages and compares the cysts with hailstones. The larval stage in the pig was so well known in the fifth century B.C., that Aristophanes, in his play the *Knights* refers to the examination of the tongues of pigs for diagnosis. Hippocrates was familiar with hydatid disease in man and Galen was acquainted with hydatids in slaughtered animals. He wrote " The liver is very much inclined to produce hydatids in the surrounding fascia. Sometimes the liver of slaughtered animals is full of them ".[67] Aretaeus also knew hydatid disease in man for he recorded in some cases of swelling of the abdomen for which paracentesis was performed, that the puncture wound became stopped up with vesicles, a circumstance which indicates the puncture of an *Echinococcus* cyst containing daughter vesicles. The nature of these cysts was not however in the least understood and any cystic swelling was called a hydatid. No further advances were made throughout the Middle Ages but, with increasing interest in natural history during the sixteenth century, the presence of cystic structures in a wide variety of animal species was noted. Occasional cases of human infection were recorded and some of these are quoted in the well-known compilation "Sepulchretum sive anatomica practica" of Bonetus, published in 1697. Here, for example, is quoted the case of a soldier with multiple subcutaneous cysts on the arms and thighs and another of liver abscess from which fell out more than 200 vesicles when it was opened.[68]

A famous case of hydatid disease of the liver was that of the first Earl of Shaftesbury, which was well recorded in manuscript by his personal physician, John Locke. Although Locke never published an account of this case and so can have had but little influence on the knowledge of the subject, he would certainly have discussed it with his friend Thomas Sydenham and other London physicians. The details of this case have been published by Sir William Osler from the manuscript notes in the Public Records Office and are of sufficient interest to be worth considering here.[69] Shaftesbury was known to have had a palpable tumour in the hypochondrium for at least 12 years prior to May, 1668, from which he suffered no inconvenience. He then began to experience severe abdominal pain and vomiting and there "suddenly sprung up below the ensiform cartilage a soft tumour the size of an ostrich egg. It was yielding to the touch, but on being compressed it did not for a moment retain any traces of the fingers". On June 12th, after consultation between the physicians and surgeons, "it was opened by the application of cautery". A large quantity of purulent matter was discharged and also "many bags and skins". Four days later "a great quantity of matter came forth, with many bags to ye number of at least 80". The opening was kept dilated with wax candles and "spung tents". Sloughs, purulent matter and little bags continued to be discharged for nearly three weeks but then no more "bags". The abscess continued to drain for another three weeks with gradual improvement, the discharge changing in character until it consisted of no more than "some pretty laudable yellowish matter" and finally of "little matter and not yellowish". At this stage there was a discussion as to whether to allow the abscess opening to heal or artificially to keep it open for free drainage. The most eminent physicians of London were consulted including Sydenham, Glisson and Sir George Ent and it was decided to keep a permanent silver drainage tube *in situ.* Shaftesbury's "spigot" became famous in contemporary literature and much amused the wits of King Charles II's court. A special sort of wine vessel with a turncock was called a " Shaftesbury " and his common nickname was " Tapski ". Dryden described him in the following lines:

> " The working ferment of his active mind
> in his weak body's cask confined
> would burst the rotten vessel where tis 'bent
> but that tis tapped to give the treason vent."

and Carryl wrote:

> " The silver pipe is no sufficient drain
> for the corruption of this little man."

However, the treatment seems to have been successful and Shaftesbury survived for nearly 15 years more.

At this time the nature of the cysts was completely unknown and various theories were put forward such as that they were: enlarged and degenerated glands, accumulations of pus mixed with serum, altered ends of blood vessels, lymphatic varices, serum accumulations in cellular tissue or degenerated mucus sacs.[70]

Towards the end of the seventeenth century an important advance was made: the animal nature of the cysts was discovered. This discovery was made independently by at least three men who noted independent, undulatory movements when the cysts were placed in warm water. This fact was first published by F. Redi in 1684, and at the same time he recognized the similarity of these cysts from different animals which he grouped together under the name " Gladulette o vesichette verminose ". In the following year a Königsberg surgeon, by the name of Hartmann, noted the living nature of a cysticercus from a goat and in 1688 that of the pig. These observations, however, remained generally unknown and were rediscovered by Tyson in 1691.[71]

Two other important observations were made in the seventeenth century, both by Johann Wepfer. Wepfer was a great physician and pathologist whose main contribution to medicine was his demonstration, in 1658, that some forms of apoplexy are due to cerebral haemorrhage. He was a Swiss and practised all his life in his native town where he was granted the unusual privilege of conducting autopsies. In this work he was assiduous and he was indeed a prodigious worker. He rose at 4 a.m., seldom went to bed before 11 p.m., and was never idle.[72] He discovered the *Cysticercus fasciolaris* of the mouse and at the same time noted its similarity with the tapeworm. He also reported cysticerci in connection with a pathological condition, in the brain of sheep suffering from the well known condition of the " staggers " or the " gid ".[73]

During the first half of the eighteenth century the animal nature of the cysticerci became gradually accepted and they came to be regarded as encysted tapeworms. This view was confirmed and fully stated by Pallas, in 1760, who pointed to the close similarity of the scolex of the encysted worm and the head of the tapeworm. He however regarded all cystic worms from various animals as a single species, *" Taenia hydatigena "*, variations in appearance being due to the different hosts. He was also aware of the very close resemblance of the head of the cystic worm of the mouse with the head of the tapeworm of the cat considering that the cat tapeworm had gone astray in the mouse.[74] Pallas also thought that animal experiment might shed light on the nature of worms and actually introduced the eggs of a tapeworm into the abdominal cavity of a dog and claimed that short tapeworms developed. This was, of course, an erroneous observation. Bloch suggested that a special species *" Vermis vesicularis "* be set up for the cystic worms but otherwise contributed little. However, Göze in 1782 in his *Versuch einer Naturgeschichte der Eingeweidewürmer tierischer Körper* made a number of interesting suggestions and observations. He believed in the zoological independence of the cystic worms but nevertheless regarded them as amongst the taenia distinguishing them as *T. visceralis* from the *T. intestinalis*. He described several species of them such as *T. visceralis hydatigenae* (cysticercus). He was, like Pallas, aware of the similarity of the heads of tape and cystic worms, in particular recognizing the similarity of the heads of cystic worms of the mouse and the tapeworm of the cat. Writing of the tapeworm of the cat he says, " The size, form and structure of the heads are perfectly identical with those of the head of the articulated cystic tapeworm in the liver of the mouse . . . But who can say why these two species are so similar as regards to the head and so heterogeneous in the rest of their economy?". He also discovered the relation of the *Echinococcus* cyst to its tapeworm.[75]

Göze also made some important observations on the earliest stages in the development of the cystic worm in the liver of a mouse, and considered the use of animal experiments, suggesting that the *Taenia* of warm blooded animals should be transferred to cold blooded animals, and vice versa, to see whether they changed their character or degenerated.

But with the work of Göze, progress in knowledge of the cystic worms ceased. Zeder, in 1803, formed a distinct family for the cystic worms and Rudolphi constituted them a separate order. E. S. Leuckart and F. Müller, as late as 1836, contended in vain against the authority of Rudolphi and it was not until the publication of Steenstrup's theory of alternation of generations in 1842 that the truth began to become apparent.[76]

As a result of Steenstrup's theory, Dujardin in his *Histoire naturelle des helminthes* (1845) first asserted that the cystic worms were undeveloped, young forms of tapeworms but thought that their condition was due to their having, by accident, got into the parenchyma of the body instead of the intestines, and because of the abnormal habitat developed as cystic worms. In Germany von Siebold supported Dujardin's views stating that " the cystic worms are nothing else than undeveloped and larvae-form tapeworms ", but he went on to say that he was convinced " the cystic worms are strayed tapeworms which have remained undeveloped and become degenerated ". He quoted the identical appearances of the cystic worms of the mouse and the tapeworm of the cat in support of his views. " It is certain," says he, " that single individuals of the brood of *Taenia crassicollis* frequently stray into rodent animals and here degenerate into *Cysticercus fasciolaris*, but when their host has been devoured by a cat, and they themselves thus transplanted to their proper soil, they may cast off their degenerated segments, return to the normal form of *Taenia crassicollis* and arrive at sexual maturity ". This quotation clearly puts von Siebold's views and even as late as 1850 he wrote, " that the cystic worms are really only (strayed) tapeworms ", and that with the exception of *Cysticercus fasciolaris* and perhaps *Cysticercus crispus* " no other cestode-nurse which has degenerated into a cystic worm can so far return to its normal conditions from its dropsical state, as to become fit for the production of sexual individuals ".[77]

Von Siebold was one of the most distinguished biologists of the nineteenth century and was even referred to by van Beneden as " the prince of helminthologists ". He was born in 1804, the son of a professor at Berlin University and was himself educated there under Rudolphi. He qualified in medicine but zoology, particularly invertebrate zoology, was his main interest. He did practise medicine for a few years, purposely setting up in Danzig where he had good opportunities for the study of marine animals. As a result of his writings he was appointed first professor of anatomy and physiology at Erlangen, later succeeded Purkinje at Breslau and finally held the chair of zoology and comparative anatomy at Munich until his death in 1885. His main work was a textbook of comparative anatomy published in 1846 in conjunction with his friend Stannius. Von Siebold wrote the section on the invertebrates, establishing himself as one of the foremost workers in this field. He also founded, in association with Kölliker, the *Zeitschrift für wissenschaftliche Zoologie* in 1852.[78]

In 1850 the Belgian zoologist, P. J. van Beneden, suggested that the head of the tapeworm developed directly from the egg of the worm. If the egg arrived in the intestine of a suitable animal the complete worm developed but if, in some unspecified way, it reached other tissues the head would develop, but unable to complete its growth to the mature worm, a period of rest as a cystic worm would ensue. Van Beneden also compared the cystic worms with the larvae of another genus of parasite, *Tetrarhynchus,* which he had found in the gut of sharks, some still encysted in the shark's food and others in various stages of development towards the adult attached to the mucosa of the shark's intestine.[79].

It was at this point, in the year 1851, that Kuchenmeister conceived the idea of feeding the cystic worms to various animals to see if they developed into tapeworms. He chose first the cystic worms most readily available to him; the *Cysticercus pisiformis* of the rabbit and the *Cysticercus fasciolaris* of the mouse. These he fed to a dog and cat respectively, and showed that tapeworms approaching maturity developed in their intestines. He was thus able to state that " the cystic worms constitute a necessary step in the development of the *Taeniae* ". At the same time he demonstrated that there was an element of host specificity, for the *Taeniae* from *Cysticercus pisiformis* failed to mature in the intestine of the cat and died within a short time.[80]

Kuchenmeister's experiments were immediately repeated, particularly by von Siebold and his pupils. Von Siebold was doubtless not a little chagrined to have missed making such an important discovery, particularly as he was an eminent professor and Kuchenmeister but a general practitioner and amateur parasitologist. Von Siebold lost no opportunity in trying to rob the latter of at least some of the credit but seems to have added nothing of importance to Kuchenmeister's discovery.

How did man become infested with tapeworms? With the essential clue provided by Kuchenmeister's experiments a little reflection clearly pointed to the answer. The head of the common tapeworm, *T. solium,* was evidently similar to the scolex of the *Cysticercus cellulosae* of the pig. Kuchenmeister appreciated that this tapeworm was unknown amongst those who did not use the pig as food, such as Jews and Moslems. He knew also that *T. solium* infestation was particularly common amongst the butchers of Germany and their families. The butchers contaminated their hands and knives, particularly when making pork sausages, infected themselves, their families and even their customers with cysticerci transferred to other cuts of meat. Indeed Kuchenmeister's wife had found cysticerci in the water she used to wash some sausages. The pathway of human infection seemed clear; it required but direct experiment to establish the point with certainty; and from this experiment Kuchenmeister did not shrink. He obtained permission, in 1854, to perform a feeding experiment on a murderer condemned to death. For three days before execution the criminal was fed numerous cysticerci partly in rice or vermicelli soup carefully cooled to blood heat, and partly in blood puddings from which the fat was removed and replaced by cysticerci. On dissection two days after execution, Kuchenmeister found, in the small intestine, 10 young tapeworms some of which had attached themselves with their hooks to the intestinal mucosa. The worms were only 4-8 mm. long and appeared just as the tapeworms in the dog following the administration of the rabbit cysticerci. Five years later he repeated the experiment feeding cysticerci to a prisoner in November who was not executed until the end of the following March by which time he harboured 19 well-developed tapeworms.[81]

Thus far the life-cycle of the tapeworm had become clear—they developed from the cysticercal stage which occurred in an intermediate host. However, the development of the cysticerci from the eggs of the tapeworm had yet to be demonstrated. This stage in the life-cycle was first observed by Stein (1818-1885), a professor at Prague, who saw the embryos of a species of tapeworm in the gut of a mealworm beetle break out of their egg shell, penetrate the intestinal wall, become encysted and then increase in size as the tapeworm scolex formed.[82] Meanwhile Kuchenmeister was working on this aspect of the problem by administering eggs to animals. He first fed a dog with the eggs of *T. solium,* being misled by an earlier report of *Cysticercus cellulosae* in dogs. Kuchenmeister knew that *Cysticercus cellulosae* must be very uncommon in dogs and therefore if he succeeded in producing the condition it would be a particularly convincing experiment. However, the experiment produced negative results. A similar trial in rabbits failed. He tried feeding the eggs of a tapeworm from a thrush and a starling to mealworms, but again without positive results. Kuchenmeister had by this time some appreciation of the host specificity of these parasites. In 1853 he resolved to work with *T. coenurus* because it was well known that the cystic stage in sheep produced the characteristic vertigo of the " gid " in infected animals. Obtaining some coenurus cysts from sheep he fed them to dogs and some two months later the dog was passing mature proglottides. These were administered to a perfectly healthy, two year old sheep, of a breed not usually affected with " gid ". In less than a month the animal was so ill with vertigo that it had to be killed, and in the brain Kuchenmeister found the characteristic coenurus cysts. The result of this experiment was clearly of great economic importance and when Kuchenmeister reported his results to the Saxon Ministry of the Interior, Professor Haubner of the veterinary school at Dresden, was commissioned to test his conclusions. The experiment was repeated in six lambs in the January of 1854. Five of them became vertiginous in 11 days. This striking result was rapidly confirmed by many workers. Kuchenmeister himself sent proglottides of *T. coenurus* in egg white to Gurlt in Berlin, Eschricht in Copenhagen, van Beneden in Louvain, Leuckart in Giessen and Roll in Vienna, all of whom produced vertigo in sheep. Although the full migration of the embryo from the gut to the brain had not so far been observed, the inference that they in fact did so was inescapable. Almost immediately Leuckart reported that mice fed with the eggs of *T. crassicollis* developed cystic worms and it was shown by van Beneden, towards the end of 1853, that *Cysticercus cellulosae* developed in the pig after the administration of *T. solium* proglottides. Kuchenmeister in collaboration with Professor Haubner repeated these experiments and succeeded, in one experiment, in rendering a whole litter of piglets measly but cysts failed to develop in some pigs fed with the eggs of *T. solium.*[83]

The most important type of cestode infestation in man was, and still is, hydatid disease and early descriptions of this condition have been mentioned. It must be pointed out that the similar nature of hydatids and bladderworms was not originally recognized. On the contrary, hydatid cysts were grouped with various other cysts of diverse origin, such as ovarian cysts, polycystic kidneys and hydatidiform moles. Although the animal nature of the bladderworm cysts in animals had been clearly pointed out in the seventeenth century, even this was not generally accepted. Morgagni, for example, considered that the fact that the cyst fluid did not coagulate on heating was against this view.[84] Pallas in 1767 first recognized hydatids as independent organisms allied to the bladderworms and Göze even described their contained heads. However, subsequent observers were not successful in their search for heads and denied their existence.[85]

Matthew Baillie at the end of the eighteenth century wrote, " The origin and real nature of these hydatids are not fully ascertained: it is extremely probable, however, that they are a sort of imperfect animalcule. There is no doubt that the hydatids in the livers of sheep are animalcules; they have often been seen to move when taken out of the liver and put into warm water, . . . The analogy is very strong between hydatids in the liver of sheep and in the human subject ". The fact that human hydatids had never been seen to move did not surprise him; they were rare and the delay between death and autopsy could account for this. He also noted, " it appears even more difficult to account for their production according to the common theory of generation, than that of intestinal worms "[86]

Laennec, in 1804, presented, at the Société de la Faculté de Médecine de Paris, his " Mémoire sur les vers vesiculaires, principalement ceux qui se trouvent dans le corps humain ". In this paper he reviewed the various bladderworms occurring in animals and illustrated them with his own drawings. The most important point in this memoir was his creation of a distinct species, the " acephalocyst ", for hydatids in which no evidence of developing heads could be found. Because of the great authority of Laennec, this type of cyst was accepted as distinct from the others for many years, until it was proved by Livois, in 1843, that it was but the ordinary hydatid in which the scolices had not yet developed.[87] In 1837 Richard Bright reported the results of his pathological studies on 15 cases of human hydatid disease but as regards their actual nature he wrote, " Of the origin of hydatids we are so completely ignorant, that it would be vain to hazard a conjecture on the subject. They are believed to be independent animals, existing without any vascular connection with the body in which they are developed; but whence the ova are derived, how introduced into the body, is altogether unknown ".[88]

Hydatid cysts were obviously different from the other bladderworms in that the scolices were budded off in special brood capsules and no movements could be observed. Rudolphi and the earlier workers thought that they constituted two species: *Echinococcus hominis* which contained numerous daughter cysts and *Echinococcus veterinorum* which was a simple cyst. It was later shown by F. S. Leuckart, Creplin and von Siebold that this distinction was not valid and there was but a single species.[89] Kuchenmeister revived the idea of there being two species, basing his distinction on the number and size of the hooklets on the scolices. R. Leuckart later showed that these differences depended upon the age of the cyst. It is strange that a helminthologist of Kuchenmeister's ability should have been led astray in this way and that he should have persisted in his error for so long. He considered that there were two types of *Echinococcus,* one which he called *E. scoliciipariens* which had a dog to sheep or cattle life-cycle, but which might infect man instead of the sheep. The other *E. altricipariens* was derived from a tapeworm living in the human intestines and which was probably identical with the rare *Hymenolepis nana,* which had been described by Bilharz and von Siebold. This tapeworm was also capable of infesting the dog. It was easy to see how man became infested with the cysts of *E. scoliciipariens,* by getting involved in the dog to sheep cycle, where sheep rearing was a main means of livelihood and people lived in too intimate an association with their dogs. But how man became infested with *E. altricipariens* was less easy. He suggested three possible mechanisms: first, that the *Taenia* eggs might be passed from the dog to man, second, that the eggs be passed from man to man, and thirdly, that a man with an *E. altricipariens* cyst might have it rupture into the bowel and mature *Taenia* develop there.

Because of the prevalence of echinococcus cysts amongst the Icelanders, Kuchenmeister suggested " It is now a problem for the surgeons of Iceland, in the dissection of individuals who have suffered from *Echinococcus,* and especially those from whom echinococcus vesicles had passed off externally, to see whether a *Taenia* occurs in the intestinal canal of the Icelanders, agreeing in the form of its head and in its sucking discs with the second species of *Echinococcus* ".[90] He also postulated that dogs became infested with the human species of worm from a man whose daughter cysts had been discharged in faeces, in vomit, coughed up or removed by the surgeon at the operation of tapping, and left carelessly about. He again suggested that Icelandic medical men were the ones to settle this point and that they should send the intestines of sheepdogs, from families with hydatid cysts, to Copenhagen for examination. He also added that he " would also thankfully receive consignments of this kind ".

This mature tapeworm was, of course, never found and Davaine, in reviewing the problem quotes 40 cases in which a hydatid cyst had ruptured into the bowel and yet no adult tapeworm had been found. In fact Kuchenmeister's complicated view of the situation was never widely accepted, most people preferring the simpler notion that there was but one sort of cyst which might occur in either sheep or man and an adult worm which was harboured by the dog. It so happened that the adult *Echinococcus* had been known for some years. Rudolphi had first described this minute tapeworm, only a few millimetres long, in enormous numbers amongst the intestinal villi of a pug dog. They were, however, regarded as young forms of the common tapeworm of the dog just arisen by spontaneous generation from the intestinal villi. It was not until 1850 that van Beneden recognized them as a distinct species. It was von Siebold who first appreciated the relationship between the worm and the cysts of *Echinococcus veterinorum* and in 1852 instituted a feeding experiment to prove this. Kuchenmeister almost immediately confirmed this work.[91] Kuchenmeister and others tried to infect dogs with human hydatid cysts obtained at autopsy but always with negative results, presumably because the material was not sufficiently fresh. However in 1863, Naunyn obtained a positive result by feeding dogs with human cysts obtained fresh by tapping a cyst during life.[92]

The clinical and economic importance of cestode infection

It was not until about the middle of the nineteenth century when the life-cycle of the cestodes had been elucidated, that serious attempts were made to assess the size of the problem in terms of the effects of infestation on the health of man and his domestic animals. It is true that the bills of mortality, published since the early part of the seventeenth century, indicate "worms" as being a cause of death, but since the cause was diagnosed by "ancient matrons" with no real medical knowledge, the term may well have no helminthological connotation. For what it is worth, to take a typical year, 1630, out of 9,237 deaths in the City of London 31 are ascribed to worms. It was not until 1837 that mortality statistics, as accurate as the medical knowledge of the times could permit, began to be kept in England. William Farr's fourth report, for 1840, classifies helminth infections into the various species involved. In that year, with a population of sixteen million, 737 persons are said to have died of worms. Farr was in the habit of making comments on the facts displayed in his mortality tables, some of which are worth quoting: Thus in 1860, "Worms and other parasitic diseases, so rare now and so common in the Middle Ages, were the cause of 167 deaths ". In 1861, " It is worthy of remark that girls suffer more than boys from worms; thus the deaths of 71 girls and only 41 boys under five years of age, were referred to worms, and in after life an equal proportion prevails, The female tissues perhaps form the the most fruitful nidus for parasites ". In 1862, " Parasitic diseases diminish with the progress of cleanliness; worms enter the body through water generally, and sometimes through diseased meat: 156, chiefly children, died of worms. Should arrangements be made to dispose of the sewage of towns, and to supply houses with pure water, we may hope to see the deaths by worms diminish ".[93]

In 1864, the Privy Council commissioned J. L. W. Thudicum to investigate the frequency of parasitic infection in meat supplied to the London markets, assess the danger to public health and report on effective measures of prevention. Thudicum was one of the most versatile of workers in medicine. Best known as a pioneer chemical pathologist, he made his living as an ear, nose and throat surgeon. He was also a very competent parasitologist, having taken the trouble to gain personal experience of trichiniasis outbreaks in Germany and to study under Leuckart.

During an eight month period he " made a great number of observations on markets, in slaughter houses, offal shops, and other places for the sale of animal foods, including slaughter houses for horses ". He also made " such experiments as seemed necessary for the verification of disputed or the elucidation of obscure points . . . ". He was on the whole impressed by the high quality of the meat supplied to the markets but abuses there certainly were. The management and workers in the markets, although on the surface co-operative, did their best to minimize the quantity of diseased meat and would hastily destroy it on Thudicum's approach. All the slaughter houses he examined were " in an objectionable condition ". They were for the most part too small and there was an amount of uncleanliness " of which no conception can be formed except by ocular inspection ". Blood and filth all over the floors, barrels of putrefying, stinking blood and, where the meat was washed, he " conceived that it would be much cleaner to eat the tongue unwashed than to have it dipped in such an unsavoury colouring pool ".

'heodor Maximilian Bilharz (1825-1862). (From :. Olpp (1932): *Hervorragende Tropenärzte,* München: Otto Gmelin.)

Rudolph Leuckart (1822-1898). *Parasitology,* 1922 *14*.

Griffith Evans (1835-1935). (*Med. Life,* 1931, *38,* 310.) Copyright.

T. R. Lewis (1841-1886) (from his *Physiological and Pathological Researches,* 1888).

PLATE VIII

[To face p. 48

Sir Algernon Phillips Withiel Thomas (1857-1937). From a photograph taken on his 80th birthday. (From Reinhard, Edward G.: Landmarks in Parasitology, I in *Exp. Parasit.*, 1957. p. 6.

Theobald Smith (1859-1934). (From *Obituary Notices of Fellows of the Royal Society*. 1935.)

Fritz Schaudinn (1871-1906). (From the series of portraits published by Deschiens.)

George Henry Falkiner Nuttall (1862-1937). (From Anton Mansch: *Med. Wld. c.* 1906. Berlin-Charlottenburg: Eckstein.)

PLATE IX

To face p. 49]

There were in fact inspectors of meat at the London markets with powers to condemn unfit meat. But there were only four of them, two of whom had other duties, and they only operated within the city itself. There was no inspection of meat at markets just outside the city boundary, such as Camden Town, Whitechapel or Westminster, and there the unscrupulous dealer could sell all the diseased meat he wished. Moreover, the meat inspectors claimed that their position was very difficult. The small scale of their activities can be judged from the amount of meat actually condemned, about 100 tons per annum out of an estimated 80,000 tons sold. Despite these unsatisfactory conditions, Thudicum was able to find very little evidence of parasitic infection. Thus of many English pigs he saw slaughtered only one was found to be measly, although he was warned that when Irish pigs were slaughtered he would see plenty. He did not find measles in any of the pigs imported from the Continent. During the whole of his investigation he did not encounter a single case of measles in cattle but this he recognized as a much more difficult condition to diagnose since the animals were never as heavily infested as the pigs. In Thudicum's opinion " an improved diagnosis of diseased meat is one of the requirements of the progress of sanitary science. It can be furnished only by united efforts of the morbid anatomist, microscopist and chemist ".[94] Thudicum's investigations showed that however unsatisfactory it was from the point of view of cleanliness, there was not a great deal, parasitologically, to complain of in the London meat supply.

Indeed in most of the more civilized parts of Europe cestode infection was not a serious problem. Thus in one hospital in Vienna of 3,864 patients 206 had tapeworms. For tapeworm infestation to be widespread demands highly unsanitary conditions; pigs and cattle must have free access to human faeces and meat must be consumed in a raw or very much undercooked state. Such conditions did exist in several parts of the world. Almost 100 per cent. of Abyssinians were infested with *T. saginata;* indeed they regarded infestation as a normal condition and considered it unhealthy not to have a tapeworm. This high degree of infestation was readily attributable to the filthy living conditions and the fact that the Abyssinians preferred to eat their beef " fresh and raw, and, if possible, still warm and quivering ".[95] Similar conditions and habits prevailed amongst certain Cossack troops stationed at Irkutsk and a report of 130 autopsies showed only two with no tapeworm present.[96]

Tapeworm infestation was likewise a problem amongst British troops stationed in India, particularly in the Punjab, where after a two year residence, up to one-third of the men might harbour *T. saginata*. A number of valuable investigations were made by British army medical officers. It was two army doctors, Fleming and Oliver, who first proved that *T. saginata* was acquired by eating measled beef which they fed to a Moslem groom and, surreptitiously, to "a boy of low Hindoo caste" both of whom developed tapeworm.[97] The amount of infected meat supplied to the British army varied considerably. T. R. Lewis, who investigated the matter in Calcutta, could find no evidence of measles in the slaughterhouses but the managers were not co-operative. His first experience of the condition was in a piece of cold sirloin of beef placed before him at breakfast one morning. He later obtained some living cysticerci and conducted some useful investigations on the temperature required to kill them. There was considerable doubt about this, some people even maintaining that the temperature of boiling water was insufficient. These differences of opinion were due to the difficulty of determining the death of the larvae. Lewis devised an ingenious technique, applying an electric shock to the larvae under the microscope and observing whether or not the animal contracted. This worked very satisfactorily except when the electric current accidentally made contact with the brass of the microscope giving Lewis a severe shock in the eye which caused him to give up microscopy for several days. Nonetheless, he clearly established that a temperature of 130 degrees Fahrenheit, but not less, for five minutes effectively killed the cysticerci and that at temperatures less than this the meat appeared noticeably underdone and was unlikely to be eaten.[98] In the Punjab infected meat seems to have been much commoner than in Calcutta. In the single month of January 1869, at the ration stand of the Royal Artillery and 92nd Highlanders at Jullunder, 4,062 lb. of beef were condemned as measled.[99]

Much more serious than tapeworm infestation was hydatid disease, but again the incidence of the disease was very variable in different parts of the world. The conditions necessary to engender this disease are that the parasite should be freely circulated between the dog and sheep, and that man should become interposed in the cycle in place of the sheep, by living in too intimate a contact with his dogs. As Leuckart pointed out, " The explanation of the variable frequency of the *Echinococcus* is always to be found in the different occupations and modes of life of the inhabitants. The extent to which cattle and sheep are reared, the number and treatment of dogs and the varying degree of cleanliness are the principal factors by which it is determined ".[100] Thudicum wrote, " This bladderworm is one of the most dangerous and incurable parasitic diseases of man " and that " the best and richest can perish from a disease which is commonest amongst the privileged of squalor, dirt and poverty ".[101]

The recorded deaths from hydatid disease in England and Wales between 1837 and 1880 never exceeded 60 a year and were usually much less.[102] Sheep were however commonly affected, Thudicum's impression being that about half harboured *Echinococcus* cysts. The most severely affected part of the world during the nineteenth century was undoubtedly Iceland. It was estimated that there were about 10,000 cases of hydatid disease on the island at any one time and many doctors had upwards of 100 patients suffering from this condition. Circumstances were very favourable for the transmission of the disease, sheep and cattle raising being the chief industry, hygienic conditions leaving much to be desired and every peasant owning about six dogs.[103] With the growth of sheep farming in the colony of Victoria, Australia, hydatid disease rapidly became a serious problem there. The first cases of hydatid disease were reported amongst shepherds in Melbourne in 1863. By 1867 the disease was described as " exceedingly common " and between the years of 1867-1877 there were 307 deaths due to this condition out of a population of about 800,000. Estimates of the incidence amongst the sheep put the figure at about 5 per cent.[104]

Chapter III

FASCIOLA HEPATICA

ADULT digenetic trematodes occur in all groups of vertebrates although they are scarce in the elasmobranchs and commonest among the teleosts and birds. There are probably no strictly human species of trematode, and indeed, except for the schistosome, trematodes are relatively unimportant parasites of man. Nonetheless the story of the discovery of some of these parasites is of sufficient interest to be worth the telling and there is, amongst the trematodes, one of the "great" parasites of the world, *Fasciola hepatica*. Although this parasite infects man very infrequently it has been known as an important parasite of sheep since medieval times and the development of our knowledge of its life cycle constitutes a classical piece of parasitology without which no history of the subject would be complete.

The first mention of the liver fluke occurs in a treatise on the management of sheep written in the fourteenth century by a Frenchman, Jean de Brie. He was familiar with the liver rot of sheep which at the time, and for some centuries to come, was ascribed to the toxic effects of feeding on certain plants and the worms considered to be engendered in the process of decay. The earliest recognizable description of the liver fluke is said to be that of Sir Anthony Fitzherbert in a book on husbandry published in 1523. Fitzherbert, in a section of the book, devoted to knowing "rotten shepe", having dealt with various clinical findings during life remarked "whan thou hase kylde a shepe . . . if thou cut the lyver, therein wyll be lyttell quickens lyke flokes, and also the lyver, wyll be full of knottes and whyte blisters . . .".[105] A number of the writers during the sixteenth and early seventeenth centuries mention the liver rot and liver flukes in sheep and it is clear that sometimes there were extensive epidemics of the disease, as for example, in 1562, when there occurred "an unspeakable pestilence of flocks in Holland, arising everywhere through worms in the region of the liver".

Francesco Redi was the first to illustrate the liver fluke in 1668 and his researches appear to have stimulated others to investigate the liver rot and its relation to liver flukes. In 1698 Godvard Bidloo, professor of anatomy at the Hague and physician to King William III of England, published a short book on the subject. He described the anatomy of the fluke in detail, in fact in too much detail, describing both eyes and a heart. He also saw the eggs of the fluke and was firmly of the opinion that the worms were not spontaneously generated but came from the eggs which the sheep swallowed. He also doubted whether the flukes migrated up the bile ducts and postulated that they entered the blood stream and were carried to the liver. He regarded the flukes as definitely pathogenic, damaging their host by corroding the parts, appropriating nutriments of the body and fouling the body with their excrement.[106] A. Leeuwenhoek was interested in the origin of liver flukes but his views were in general less scientific than those of his friend Bidloo. He thought it likely that the sheep swallowed the flukes in water and that they migrated up the bile ducts because they were " pleased with the taste ". In August 1698 he tried to verify his hypothesis by examining water from pastures where sheep were affected by the liver rot. He described a number of animalcules but recognized that none corresponded to the liver fluke. Indeed he appears to have lost interest in the flukes as he examined these other creatures.[107] In the summer of 1702 he resumed his researches, this time examining " Pieces of greensod " since he now doubted whether the sheep acquired the parasites from water. Again he found no creatures corresponding to the liver fluke but happily investigated a variety of animals which he did find.[108]

Throughout the eighteenth century virtually nothing was added to our knowledge of the liver fluke although the subject attracted some interest because of its economic importance. Linnaeus gave the parasite its name, *Fasciola hepatica,* but regarded it as a fresh water leech which had been swallowed accidentally. Pallas described the first definite case of human infection which he saw at autopsy of a woman in 1760.[109] It was not until 1808 that Rudolphi finally separated the the flukes from the leeches and created the class of trematodes, which he defined as flat worms with ventral suckers. He classified these parasites on the basis of the number of suckers present as monostomes, distomes, etc. By 1845 over 160 species of trematodes were known from a wide variety of animals, but chiefly from birds.[110]

Meanwhile some observations relating to the life of the trematodes in general had been made. Cercariae had been observed in water by late eighteenth century microscopists who regarded them as *Infusoria*. However, Professor Nitzsch of Halle who observed their encystment also recognized their anatomical similarity with the trematodes. In 1818 Ludwig Bojanus, a professor at Wilna and comparative anatomist of invertebrates noticed, whilst dissecting some fresh water snails that they harboured what he called "royal-yellow worms" (rediae) inside which were broods of cercariae. He also observed the hatching out of the cercariae. In 1831 Karl Mehlis, a medical practitioner in Clausthal in the Harz Mountains, saw the hatching of the eggs of a trematode with the liberation of the ciliated miracidium, and in 1837 Friedrich Creplin first observed the ciliated miracidium of *Fasciola hepatica*. In 1842 Steenstrup published his treatise on *Alternations of Generations* giving as one of his examples the various trematode larvae found in fresh water snails and it became widely realized that some mollusc, in all probability, formed the intermediate host of *Fasciola hepatica*. Indeed Bradley, professor of botany in Cambridge, had as early as 1729 noted that snails and slugs were often abundant in dangerous pastures and had postulated that eating them caused liver rot.

Although the finger of suspicion pointed to a molluscan intermediate host for the liver fluke, which species of mollusc remained a mystery. Liver rot was very common in the Faroe Islands, the molluscan fauna of which was limited to eight species, and might have therefore provided a terrain with the problem somewhat simplified. In 1873 Willemoes-Suhm drew attention to this fact and suggested one species, *Limax agrestis*, the common grey slug as the intermediate host. In the following year David Weinland observed nurse forms of a trematode in *Limnaea truncatula* which he observed to hatch out as cercariae and encyst, and correctly suggested that this species was the intermediate host of the liver fluke. He did not however prove his point nor were his views accepted. As late as 1880 George Rolleston, Linacre professor of anatomy and physiology at Oxford, suggested that the black slug *Arion ater* was, in fact, the intermediate host.

But although Rolleston was here in error he was the means by which the problem was finally solved. In the summer of 1880 the Royal Agricultural Society offered him a grant to investigate liver rot, but not having time to undertake the work himself he recommended a 23-year-old graduate of Balliol College. A. P. Thomas, who was a demonstrator in the biology museum, for the work. Thomas began in June 1880 feeling that as "so many different molluscs had been suggested as possible intermediate hosts, it was necessary to examine the question anew, and not to be guided by the numerous conjectures already expressed . . .". He set to work along two lines: endeavouring to infect many molluscs with the miracidia of *Fasciola hepatica* and also visiting localities around Oxford where liver rot occurred, collecting all the species of molluscs he could find, and dissecting them in a search for larval trematodes. One area he chose to investigate was a group of five fields on the side of a hill, well above the reach of river floods, at Wytham. He searched the ground thoroughly by day and night, bringing home numerous species of invertebrates to search for larval trematodes. In one boggy spot he collected specimens of *Limnaea truncatula* and in one of them, on December 22nd, discovered an interesting form of cercaria. The cercaria exhibited a strong tendency to encyst on any object and corresponded in structure very closely to very young forms of *Fasciola,* some only about 1 mm. long, which Thomas had seen in the liver of a sheep. Thomas communicated his suspicions to the Royal Agricultural Society's Journal for April 1881. During the summer of 1881 he was naturally anxious to try infecting *L. truncatula* with the miracidia of *Fasciola* but because of the dryness of the summer was quite unable to obtain any specimens of the mollusc. However, in the following July the English climate obliged with floods, and the waters of the Isis brought down vast multitudes of *L. truncatula.* By placing them in water containing miracidia he was able to show that they were readily infected, whereas a number of other common molluscs were entirely ignored by the miracidia. Thomas was able to follow the whole process through its various stages from the entry of the miracidium, the formation of the sporocyst, in which developed the rediae, and the development of the cercariae within the rediae, their liberation and encystment, and he illustrated his observations with excellent drawings. Thus the whole of the life cycle of the liver fluke outside its definitive host was worked out.

At the same time as the unknown Oxford demonstrator was investigating liver rot the same subject was exercising the mind of perhaps the greatest contemporary parasitologist, R. Leuckart. Rudolph Leuckart was born in 1822; he studied medicine at Göttingen and remained there as privat-docent until 1852. His interests were zoological rather than medical and it was said that he wrote " valuable memoirs on some member of almost every class in the animal kingdom ". In 1852 he was made professor of zoology at Giessen and in 1869 went to Leipzig where he was provided with a fine new institute and museum. Here he was visited in 1884 by William Osler who wrote home " How I envy some of these men! Leuckart has about $4,000 a year with a splendid set of apartments on the third floor of the institute ".

Leuckart was industrious and of an amiable disposition and attracted pupils from many countries. He was elected foreign member of the Royal Society in 1877. His parasitological investigations covered a very wide range and many of his original observations were published in his famous *Die menschlichen Parasiten und die von ihnen herruhrinden Krankheiten* which was translated into English in 1886. He died in 1898.

In December 1881 Leuckart published a paper claiming that he had succeeded in infecting *L. pereger,* but, as Thomas had also found, development did not proceed to its normal conclusion in that host. In 1882 he reported that he had found three species of redia in *L. truncatula* one of which contained tailless embryos which he held were probably the larval form of *F. hepatica*. He did not persist long in this error. Later in the year he realized that it was one of the tailed embryos which was related to *F. hepatica* and that *L. truncatula* was the true intermediate host, and in fact, his paper appeared only 10 days before that of Thomas.

Thomas was rightly proud of his work which had been careful, accurate and without the false starts and hasty conclusions of the more famous parasitologist. It must indeed have been galling to be forestalled by so short a time and he carefully pointed out, in a lengthy historical introduction, the exact dates of the various steps in his own investigations and publications, comparing them with Leuckart's publications. Both men worked quite independently fully confirming each other's work but posterity may well be inclined to admire more the work of the young Oxonian on this occasion.[111] It is sad to record that Thomas's brilliant beginning in parasitological research did not lead to further distinguished work in this field. In 1883 he became the first professor of biology and geology in the newly established Auckland University College in New Zealand, where he became immersed in his work as a teacher and administrator which eventually earned him a knighthood. However, he never did further original work the equal of that done at the age of 23 in the sheep pastures around Oxford.

Some details in the life cycle of *Fasciola* remained to be filled in. The Brazilian, Lutz, a pupil of Leuckart, working in the Hawaiian Islands in 1892, successfully demonstrated that herbivorous animals actually became infected by eating the encysted worms. The Russian parasitologist D. F. Sinitsin in 1914, demonstrated the path taken by the larval flukes from the gut to the liver, which they invaded through the capsule, having penetrated the gut wall and migrated across the peritoneal cavity. Sinitsin was born in 1871 and at the time of his work on *Fasciola* was a professor at the Shanjasky University in Moscow and well known for his work on the trematodes of frogs and fishes. In 1923, for political reasons, he was forced to flee from his native Russia to the United States where for a time he lived in poverty. Nothing daunted, he began a career afresh, obtaining employment as a museum technician and later as a zoologist in the Bureau of Animal Industry. He died in 1937.

Chapter IV

THE SCHISTOSOMATA

DISEASE due to species of *Schistosoma* is fairly widespread in tropical and subtropical parts of the world, but was first recognized by parasitologists in Egypt. In that country infestation with *Schistosoma* is known to have existed since ancient times; its most prominent clinical manifestation, haematuria, is mentioned some 50 times in various medical papyri and calcified eggs of *Schistosoma haematobium* have been found in Egyptian mummies dating from about 1200 B.C.[112]

The first Europeans to experience schistosome infection on any scale appear to have been the soldiers of Napoleon's stranded army in Egypt (1799-1801). Baron Larrey, the famous military surgeon, noted the frequency of haematuria in the army and it is interesting that the actual intermediate host of the *Schistosoma* was illustrated in the *Description de l'Egypte* published by the French during their occupation, although, of course, its connection with the Egyptian haematuria was quite unknown.[113]

No light was shed upon the nature of the prevalent haematuria of Egypt for a further half century, until the labours of a young German parasitologist, Theodor Bilharz. He was born in 1825 at Sigmoringen on the Danube where his father was a manager on the royal estates. He was very diligent at school and early acquired a taste for natural history and collecting which was encouraged by an uncle. He studied medicine at Freiburg and Tübingen where he met Griesinger, and qualified in 1849. After spending a year back at Freiburg studying comparative anatomy, which was his main interest, he joined Griesinger in Egypt as his prosector in 1850. Here he worked with his accustomed diligence doing an average of three necropsies each day, and was particularly impressed by the opportunities his position afforded him for parasitological studies. He discovered a number of new species of human parasites and was associated with Griesinger in his observations on ankylostomiasis. But by far the most important of his discoveries was that of the schistosome worm and its relation with the endemic haematuria of Egypt. The discovery of this parasite he announced in a letter to his old teacher, von Siebold, dated May 1st, 1851. He added more details in two further letters that year and named the parasite *Distomum haematobium*. Von Siebold published extracts of these letters with his comments in a German zoological journal in 1853. Bilharz also sent his old teacher some preserved specimens of the parasite but the latter was not able to make out very much of their internal structure.[114] Bilharz's appointment in Egypt appears to have been a personal arrangement with Griesinger and when the latter returned to Germany, Bilharz's salary ceased. However, through the good offices of the German consul, he obtained a post on the surgical side of the medical school where he worked for seven years. In 1862 he accompanied the Duke of Saxe-Coburg-Gotha as his personal physician on an expedition into Abyssinia where he caught a fever, said to have been typhus, and died at the age of 37.[115]

The prevalence of this newly described parasite at autopsy in Egypt was soon shown to be very high, being present in some 30-40 per cent. of the population, although commoner in men than women.

During the next few years it was shown that this parasite was not confined to the human species or to Egypt. In 1857 Cobbold described a worm, clearly of the same genus in the body of an ape dying in the London Zoological Society's garden. At first he believed this parasite to be a distinct species, but later agreed that it appeared identical to that infecting man.[116] Cobbold pointed out that, on anatomical grounds, the parasite was clearly not a *Distomum* and that an alternative name would have to be found. Already a number of suggestions had been made, including that of *Schistosoma* by David Weinland. Cobbold, however, proposed to name the genus *Bilharzia* in memory of its discoverer, a thought which met with universal approval, Weinland being quite willing to abandon his name "*Schistosoma*".[117] For about half a century the parasite was known as *Bilharzia haematobium* and was even accorded a slang appellation as "Bill Harris" by the British soldiers serving in Egypt during the First World War. However, recent tightening up of the rules of zoological nomenclature have decreed that Weinland's three month priority with the name *Schistosoma* must stand and the parasite is now known as *Schistosoma haematobium.*

The first person to draw attention to the wider distribution of schistosomes was a London physician, John Harley. Harley had no tropical experience but saw a patient with haematuria in London, who had previously resided at the Cape of Good Hope. Under the microscope Harley found the schistosome eggs and even observed the hatching of the miracidium. His patient told him that haematuria was common in that part of the world and on consulting a doctor who had practised in the Cape, Harley found this opinion confirmed. The old doctor told him that both his sons had suffered from haematuria but were now better, but Harley, on examining their urine microscopically found schistosome eggs to be present.

Harley could hardly claim to be an expert parasitologist but he recognized the genus from the eggs and gave it as his opinion that this was a new species which he wished to call *Distomum capensis.* He gave an account of his findings at a meeting of the Royal Medical and Chirurgical Society in London in January 1864. In the discussion that followed there was some disagreement as to whether or not haematuria was particularly endemic in the Cape, the testimony of the Bishop of Natal, " whose sympathies are, perhaps as much scientific as clerical " being quoted against the proposition. Cobbold flatly disagreed that Harley's parasite was a new species and pointed out that the chief importance of his communication was the demonstration that infestation with this parasite was much more widespread than had been thought.[118]

The importance of discovering the life cycle of the parasite, from the preventive point of view, was appreciated but neither Bilharz nor Griesinger had given attention to the problem. The first serious investigations on the subject were those made by Cobbold in 1870. Cobbold obtained a supply of schistosome eggs from a little girl from Natal. He was by no means the first person to observe the hatching of the eggs but he made a careful study of the conditions under which hatching took place. He noted that the eggs showed no inclination to hatch in urine but did so regularly in water, fresh, brackish or even salt. He remarked on the similarity of the ciliated embryo with that of the liver fluke and sought to determine the species of intermediate host by placing the embryos in contact with a variety of animals " such as Gammari, Dipterous larvae, Entomostraca, Lymnaei, Paludinae, different species of Planorbis and other molluscs; but neither in these, nor in Sticklebacks, Roach, Gudgeon or Carp did they seem inclined to take up their abode ".[119]

Sonsino, in Egypt during 1884 and 1885, made a sustained effort to work out the life cycle. He appreciated the likelihood of a mollusc acting as the intermediate host and made numerous attempts to infect molluscs with miracidia without success. He also dissected large numbers of molluscs discovering many new species of cercariae but none which he could correlate with the schistosome.[120] His work was interrupted when he left Egypt in 1885 but the problem continued to intrigue him. Some seven years later he went to Tunis to resume work on the subject and his efforts were, he believed, crowned with success. He thought he saw the miracidium invade the body of a small crustacean but did not immediately publish his findings. He did however take precautions to secure for himself priority in his supposed discovery by sending a sealed letter containing his observations to a scientific society in Pisa. On transferring himself to another town where the parasite was endemic in order to confirm his findings he was unable to find specimens of his little crustacean. But he did manage to get miracidia to invade the bodies of a local insect larva and therefore concluded that the schistosoma had more than one intermediate host. His results were published in 1893.[121] Sonsino believed that infection was acquired from drinking water, pointing out that there was no parasite of man that entered the human body in any way other than by mouth.[122]

Prospero Sonsino never made any major discovery in his chosen field of medicine but was nonetheless a most enthusiastic student of parasitology. He was born in Tunis in 1835 but he was taken to Italy as a child and graduated from the University of Pisa. His life was spent wandering about North Africa and the Middle East working at a variety of problems, publishing in all 139 papers of which 70 were devoted to helminthology. He never obtained any settled academic position although in later life he gave a free course on parasitology in Pisa. He worked often under appalling and even dangerous conditions. He was in Cairo during the insurrection of 1882 and was one of the few Europeans who refused to leave, feeling it his duty to keep the hospital open. Perhaps his most important work was to emphasize the great importance of helminths as a cause of disease at a time when they were in danger of being neglected for the study of bacteria. He died in 1901.[123] By then the connection of schistosome infection with water seemed fairly well established but whether acquired by drinking water was not certain. In 1894 G. S. Brock, a practitioner in Rustenberg in the Transvaal, drew attention to the possibility of the infective form of the parasite gaining access to the body, not via the mouth but through the skin whilst bathing. He pointed out that around Rustenberg, the disease was very common in boys but infrequent in girls although both drank water from the same source. But whereas Boers of neither sex indulged in much washing, all the boys bathed in streams but the girls did not. Moreover complaint of an itching sensation of the skin after bathing was common.[124]

The problem of the life-cycle of the schistosome had meanwhile attracted the attention of A. Looss in Egypt. He repeated the attempts of Cobbold and Sonsino to infect various species of mollusc with miracidia but always with negative results. He dissected molluscs without finding any cercariae which could, on anatomical grounds, conceivably be referred to the schistosome and so felt himself obliged to conclude that the schistosome had no molluscan intermediate host. Looss believed that the miracidium was the infective stage for man, considering that the disease was directly communicable from man to man and that the miracidia developed into adult schistosomes in the liver where, indeed, young forms might be observed. Owing to Looss's great authority in helminthological matters and his skill in dialectics this view was fairly generally accepted and most research was directed to the verification of his hypothesis.[125]

Whilst work on the life-cycle of *Schistosoma haematobium* stagnated, information of interest on other aspects of the blood fluke was being accumulated. It appeared that *Schistosoma haematobium* was not the only species of that genus to infect man. For some years Japanese physicians in the province of Yamanashi, Hiroshima and Saga had recognized an endemic disease characterized by enlargement of the liver and spleen, cachexia, ascites and bloody diarrhoea, and at autopsy numerous eggs of an unknown helminth had been noted in various organs, particularly the liver. In April 1904 Professor Katsurada of the Pathological Institute of Okayama when examining faeces from a typhoid case observed the eggs and the fact that they contained a ciliated embryo which he recognized as similar to that of *S. haematobium*. Having no opportunity of making a post-mortem examination he thought of examining dogs and cats from the endemic area because he had already found that some human trematodes were not infrequently present in these animals. His search was almost immediately rewarded with the find of numerous schistosomes, containing eggs exactly like those from human cases, in the portal system of two cats from the province of Yamanashi. He published this information in August 1904 and named the new parasite *S. japonicum*. The eggs of this species were clearly distinguished from those of *S. haematobium* by the fact that they had no terminal spine. The existence of this new species was soon confirmed by Dr. John Catto of the London School of Tropical Medicine in material taken from a Chinaman dying in Singapore. At that time nothing was known of the life cycle of this parasite.[126]

Meanwhile some doubts had been raised as to whether the well-known *S. haematobium* was a single species or whether two different parasites were being confounded. From the time of Bilharz it had been known that schistosomes discharged eggs both in the urine and the faeces and it had also been observed that the eggs found in the faeces had their spines placed laterally rather than terminally. That this situation was constant had not, however, been established. The earliest observations were made on Egyptians most of whom suffered from urinary as well as rectal schistosome infestation. It was therefore not unnatural to think that a single species of parasite might lay its eggs in the veins of both rectum and bladder. The difference in character of the eggs was ignored or else very unconvincing mechanical explanations offered. Sonsino at one time raised the possibility of there being two species of schistosome but the matter was not taken up until the suggestion of Manson in the early years of the twentieth century. Manson drew attention to the fact that rectal and vesical disease were, in fact, distinct. This had been brought home to him forcibly by a case of rectal schistosomiasis in an Englishman coming from the West Indies who had never visited Africa. This man passed only laterally spined eggs in the faeces and repeated examination of his urine failed to reveal any eggs whatever. Manson found it difficult to believe that one and the same species would lay eggs with different structure in different sites in its host and in his Lane lectures of 1905 said, " I am tempted to conjecture that we may be dealing with two or more distinct species, and that the American *Bilharzia* belongs to the lateral-spined species ".[127]

The argument in favour of the two species was taken up by L. W. Sambon in 1907. He restated very fully the evidence for this point of view, the distinct anatomical types of disease, the different geographical distribution of the two clinical types and the correlation with the structurally different eggs. He proposed that the species laying laterally spined eggs should be named *S. mansoni*.[128] This view was severely criticized in a long article, written in a most acrimonious style, by Looss. He was of the opinion that it was quite unjustifiable to differentiate species solely on a difference in egg structure without showing any anatomical difference between adults. Moreover he maintained that he had seen adult female worms containing both terminal and lateral spined eggs.[129] The tone of Looss's article was undoubtedly offensive and was replied to by Sambon who again went over the evidence in favour of the two species and commented, acidly, that until Professor Looss could " show me an actual specimen I am bound to place the worm capable of producing the two kinds of eggs with the phoenix, the chimaera and other mythical monsters ".[130]

The controversy was not, however, finally settled until the elucidation of the whole life cycle of the schistosome some six years later. The life cycle and true mode of transmission of a schistosome from man to man was first demonstrated in *S. japonicum*. Between 1908 and 1910 Fujinama and Nakanura showed that mice which had been immersed in water from rice fields known to be dangerous to man became infected with *S. japonicum*. Soon after, Migairi and Suzuki infected fresh water snails with miracidia of the same species and Ogata described the cercarial stage of the parasite.[131] This work was confirmed and extended by Leiper and Atkinson who showed that cercariae were able to penetrate the skin of a mouse. This work indicated that it was almost certain that the other human schistosomes had a similar life cycle although Looss was still opposed to the idea. However, the outbreak of the First World War and the stationing of large numbers of British troops in Egypt had rendered the problem more pressing. The morbidity from schistosomiasis amongst British troops during the Boer War had been considerable and pensions to a total of £10,000 per annum were still being paid to ex-servicemen who had acquired infection at that time. The War Office, anxious to avoid similar troubles in Egypt, sent out Leiper with the rank of Lieut.-Colonel to investigate the life cycle of the schistosome in Egypt. Leiper arrived in Egypt in February 1915 and very rapidly solved the problem which had baffled so many eminent helminthologists. He first collected a complete set of Egyptian fresh water molluscs for identification, then, choosing the convenient village of El Marg, close to Cairo with a half hourly train service to and fro and where 90 per cent. of the population had schistosome eggs in their urine, set to work. Large numbers of fresh water molluscs were collected and examined for the presence of trematode larvae either by leaving them in water overnight and looking for free-swimming cercariae next day or by dissecting the livers and looking for rediae. Within a few weeks all the trematode larvae recorded for Egypt had been found as well as other undescribed types. Amongst these were cercariae "which presented the peculiar morphological features in the alimentary canal which characterized the bilharzial worms". Of the bilharzial cercariae one was considered to be of an avian species. Two other species of cercariae seemed possibly related to the human schistosome. They had been hatched respectively from a species of *Bulinus* and *Biomphalaria*.

Experimental work on the transmission of human schistosomes had been hampered by the belief, fostered by Looss, that man was the only susceptible species. Leiper remembered however that Cobbold had discovered an apparently identical schistosome in a monkey. This worm was still available in the Hunterian Museum of the Royal College of Surgeons and on examination Leiper was convinced that it was none other than the human *S. haematobium*. He therefore had sent out to Egypt a number of the same species of monkey and was soon able to infect them with cercariae from both *Bulinus* and *Biomphalaria*. The monkeys, moreover, developed clinical schistosomiasis. Leiper went on to infect, successfully, mice, rats and guinea-pigs. He was able to show that if mice were immersed in water containing cercariae the latter disappeared leaving their tails behind them and in sections could be found burrowing into the skin of the mice. There thus seemed no doubt that infection was acquired through the cercariae penetrating the skin and the observations of field workers suggesting that schistosomiasis was caused by bathing were vindicated. The other possible route of infection, per os, remained unverified. Leiper tried to infect a monkey by administering cercariae by mouth. The monkey did indeed become infected but immediately after the administration of the cercariae showed obvious signs of irritation in the mouth suggesting that the cercariae were penetrating the oral mucosa. Moreover Leiper showed that a concentration of only 1:500 hydrochloric acid rapidly killed cercariae and it was therefore unlikely that they could survive the action of the gastric juice.

Incidentally, Leiper finally settled the vexed question of the existence of two species, *S. haematobium* and *S. mansoni*. He found that cercariae hatched from *Bulinus* always gave rise in experimental animals, to adult worms which produced eggs with a terminal spine. Those hatched from *Biomphalaria* gave rise to adults producing laterally spined eggs. He was also able to show by careful anatomical studies of adult worms that the two species showed differences in the structure of both uterus and testis. The actual pathology of the infections differed also. *S. haematobium* left the liver for the vesical veins early in its development, whereas *S. mansoni* remained in the liver until relatively mature and even sometimes laid eggs there.

Thus the full life cycle of one of the most important human parasites was finally worked out almost 65 years after the first observation of the adult worm and the pathological effects of its eggs. In his work Leiper was helped by a Pte. W. McDonald who acted as his laboratory assistant and whose help he generously acknowledged—" It was mainly due to his persistent work and scientific acumen that the cercariae of the *Bilharzia haematobium* was discovered ".[132]

CHAPTER V

TRICHINELLA SPIRALIS

WE now come to consider the history of one of the most interesting of parasitic diseases—trichinosis. The story of our knowledge of this condition contains many of the elements that excite our interest in any tale of adventure. The story is a short one, less than half a century elapsing between the first inkling of the existence of the disease and a tolerably complete understandings of it.

The Mosaic and Mohammedan prohibitions on the eating of pork are far more likely to have been due to the observation of outbreaks of trichinosis than any recognition of an association with tapeworm infestation. The effects of the consumption of infected pork can be most dramatic. It is not unusual for 100 per cent. of those at risk to be taken ill within a few days with a most severe illness carrying a mortality of up to 30 per cent. The association of the disease with the eating of pork would be well within the capacity of primitive peoples. Indeed, what is surprising is that this association was lost sight of by the world at large, although the condition cannot have been uncommon, and looking back we can recognize epidemics which were almost certainly trichinosis.

The earliest observation of what were almost certainly the encysted trichinella larvae in muscle was the report of Tiedemann, in 1822, of a post-mortem examination on a man who had been a great brandy-drinker and who died after several severe attacks of gout. Tiedemann found white, stony concretions in most of the muscles, especially of the extremities. He had them examined chemically, probably thinking they were connected with the gout, and Gmelin found they were composed of phosphate and carbonate of lime and animal matter resembling albumen or fibrin.[133] Tiedemann had no inkling of the parasitic nature of his " little bodies " and an eminent student of this disease, R. Leuckart, later doubted whether Tiedemann was, in fact, dealing with a case of trichinosis. But, on balance, the evidence suggests that he was. Likewise John Hilton in 1833 reported a case of peculiar mottling of the voluntary muscles at the autopsy of a man dying of cancer. Both he and Addison attempted to elucidate their nature with the aid of the microscope but without success. Hilton did however suggest that the tiny specks might be a species of minute cysticercus.[134]

Certainly, at the time, these observations aroused no interest and the real beginning of the history of the disease can be dated precisely to the dissecting room of St. Bartholomew's Hospital, London, on February 2nd, 1835, when a 21-year-old medical student, James Paget, noticed certain little specks in the muscles of the subject he was dissecting. He reported his findings before his fellow students at the Abernethian Society on February 6th. Paget tells the story in his autobiography. He wrote: "Another event, in this first year's study, which had some influence on my later life, was the discovery of the *Trichina spiralis*. Dr. Cobbold has told the story of the several steps leading to the discovery and following it, in his latest work on the Entozoa. My share was the detection of the ' worm ' in its capsule; and I may justly ascribe it to the habit of looking at, and observing, and wishing to find new things, which I had acquired in my previous studies of botany. All the men in the dissecting-room, teachers included, ' saw ' the little specks in the muscles: but I believe that I alone ' looked at ' them and ' observed ' them: no one trained in natural history could have failed to do so. The discovery had a memorable consequence, in procuring me an introduction to Robert Brown. I wanted to examine the entozoon with a microscope and there was none in the Hospital. I thought I might get help from Mr. Children, who was the chief of the Natural History Department of the British Museum, and to whom Mr. Dawson Turner had given me a letter of introduction. He, however, had no microscope; but suggested that ' Robert Brown might help me '. So we went at once to the little room in the Museum in which the great botanist was at work among books and specimens; and I remember Mr. Children's first question, ' Brown, do you know anything about parasitic worms?' and the answer, ' No: thank God '. But he let me look at my specimens with his little single microscope —the same, I think, that he had done his own grand work with; and I made the sketches of them with which to illustrate the paper read at the Abernethian Society. This was, certainly, the first account given of the new entozoon but Owen, to whom specimens were taken when I had seen that there was a ' worm ', read a paper on it at the Zoological Society and gave it its name. It mattered little: the repute of the discovery would have been of no great use to me; and I should have gained less happiness by disputing for it and obtaining it than I have enjoyed in the personal friendship with Owen ever since. It was enough for my advantage that the discovery, and the paper at the Abernethian strengthened my position in the Hospital ".

In a letter to Dr. (later Sir William) Hooker, dated April 16th he gave some more detail; " I have enclosed a specimen and drawing (for the coarseness of which the haste in which I am obliged to make up this parcel must be my apology) of a singular animalcule which I discovered in the beginning of the year infesting the bodies of two subjects in our dissecting-room. Although not belonging to the part of natural history in which you are most interested, its novelty and extraordinary habitation may perhaps excuse my sending it to you . . . Of its causes or effects nothing can at present be said. The two subjects in which I have seen it were both very emaciated, and as far as can be remembered, this was also the case in upwards of twenty others in which the same appearances have been noticed in our dissecting-room, where they have been attributed to the deposition of small spicules of bone (which, indeed, they somewhat resemble). They do not, however, seem to produce any remarkable symptoms in the patient appreciable during life, though we can hardly imagine a single body to afford sustenance to some millions of such creatures, however minute, without some visible effect. Should any of your medical friends have seen, or hereafter meet with, analogous cases, I should be very glad to hear of them, although my time is too fully occupied with learning the discoveries of others to permit me to give up much of it to any of my own; though I cannot but feel deeply interested in following out this—although perhaps not of much importance—when so little is known of it. Not being well acquainted with the subject, I thought it best that it should be described by someone of more authority than myself, and Mr. Owen, of the College of Surgeons, read a paper on it at the Zoological Society, giving it the name of Trichina spiralis ".[135]

On February 24th, 1835, Richard Owen, then an assistant conservator of the Museum of the Royal College of Surgeons, read a paper before the Zoological Society in which he gave full credit to "Mr. Paget, an intelligent student" for observing the minute cysts and determining the existence of an entozoon. Wormold, the demonstrator of anatomy at St. Bartholomew's Hospital volunteered that he had often noticed the cysts in question but beyond noting that they blunted his scalpels, did not investigate them further. It was he who supplied Owen with material for microscopic examination. In papers published in the *London Medical Gazette* and the *Transactions of the Zoological Society* Owen gave a good description of the parasite which he illustrated with beautiful engravings. He named the worm *Trichina spiralis* and by this name it was generally known until it was pointed out, in 1896, that the name *Trichina* was already pre-occupied in zoology by a genus of *Diptera* and the name was changed to *Trichinella spiralis*.

Owen's papers aroused interest, were noted in foreign journals and reports of the conditions began to multiply. They were however merely incidental findings at autopsy and there was no suggestion that they might be associated with disease. The first person to associate *Trichinella* with disease was Henry Wood of Bristol. In 1835 he reported the case of a man suddenly afflicted with "a violent attack of acute rheumatism" who died about three weeks after the onset of his disease. Wood found the *Trichinella,* which he identified from Owen's descriptions, in the muscles at autopsy and concluded "that the presence of animals is as consistent with an acute disease as with a chronic". He endeavoured to follow up the matter and gain the help of others but was foiled "from want of proper value being set on the microscope as a means of pathological research".[136] His report went unnoticed and it was another 25 years before the pathological effects of *Trichinella* infestation were appreciated. Meanwhile the life cycle of the parasite was gradually unravelled.

The next advance in knowledge of the *Trichinella* was made by A. Farre. He made a careful microscopic examination of some worms obtained from the same source as Owen and showed that the parasite had a complex internal organization including a digestive tract and a dark granular body which he took to be ovary. He was not sure whether or not he could distinguish a mouth and anus, at least not in all specimens, but as a result of his studies he suggested that the worm was related to the round worms. He had no idea of the origin of the parasite.[137] Dujardin, in 1845, suggested that the worm might be the young stage of some other parasite, but which other parasite, he was at a loss to say and was even constrained to admit that the *Trichinella* constituted one of the strongest arguments in favour of spontaneous generation of some helminths.[138]

In 1850 Professor H. Luschke of Tübingen added considerably to knowledge of the anatomy of the parasite and also showed that the worms survived putrefaction of the surrounding flesh and also freezing. He gave an accurate description of the capsule of the worm, demonstrating the complex system of blood vessels surrounding each one and correctly stated that it was derived from a reaction of the host tissues. He described the structure of the *Trichinella* more correctly than any previous observer, showed that the pointed end and not the obtuse, thick end was the anterior end and demonstrated the true course and shape of the digestive tract. He also made out the sexual organs of the worm in its posterior end, correctly figuring the female larvae, but missed identifying the male.

In 1851 Herbst of Gottingen published a most important contribution which, unaccountably, went unnoticed at the time and has since been largely forgotten. He clearly demonstrated the transmission of trichinellae from one animal to another by feeding experiments. At this date even the use of feeding experiments in helminthology was novel and his work actually antedated by about a year Kuchenmeister's work with tapeworm cysts. Herbst had in the course of his dissections noted trichinellae in a cat and a dog and when in November 1850 a pet badger, which he had been in the habit of feeding partly with scraps from the dissecting room table, died, he found the encysted worms in all the voluntary muscles. He therefore fed some of the badger's flesh to three young puppies. Two of the puppies he killed some three months later and found an infinite number of trichinellae throughout their voluntary muscles. The third dog was in perfect health when, nine months after eating the badger's meat, Herbst exposed the sternomastoid muscle, which was normal to the naked eye, and showed under the microscope that it contained numerous encysted worms. Herbst correctly supposed, on account of the widespread and uniform distribution of the parasites in the muscles, that they were distributed by the blood stream, but he could not understand how the ova passed from the alimentary canal into the blood stream because he assumed that the ova were surrounded by a persistent egg membrane. As Thudicum remarked: "The experiments of Herbst upon the three dogs actually solved the entire question concerning the propagation of the trichinae; they showed clearly both ends of the process, and that was all that men of science could require in order at once to make sure of all the intervening stages of its process of development. But no such happy solution occurred; the experiments of Herbst in a manner fell dead, and 12 years have not sufficed to make their merit appreciated".

In fact, again to quote Thudicum, "with the year 1852 begins a period in the literature concerning trichinae which shows in a most remarkable manner the advantages and the dangers of conclusions from analogies which natural things may have with each other. The experiments of Kuchenmeister concerning the transformation of measles into taeniae gave again rise to the idea that the trichina was a juvenile form of a known nematode".[139] Kuchenmeister on the basis of similarity in the anatomy of *Trichinella* and *Trichocephalus* concluded that the relationship between the two worms was certain although he admitted that so far nobody had succeeded in rearing *Trichinellae* from *Trichocephalus* or vice versa.[140]

Leuckart went so far as to announce that he had bred *Trichocephalus* in a pig fed trichinous meat, a result clearly due to the incidental infestation of the pig with that nematode. He did not long persist in his erroneous views. He rapidly re-investigated the problem of the cycle and affinities of the *Trichinella* and published his results both as a paper and in a more extended monograph in 1860. Obtaining some trichinous human flesh in January of that year he performed two series of feeding experiments in which he showed that the *T. spiralis* of muscle was transformed in the intestine, into a small independent nematode with no relation to *Trichocephalus* and that the young of the intestinal *Trichinellae* were directly transformed into the encysted muscular form. He gave a very accurate account of the development of the adult nematode, their eggs and the hatching of the embryos which he saw penetrated the bowel wall. However he was of the opinion that the larvae migrated, not via the blood stream, but directly along inter-muscular cellular tissue. He then gave an excellent account of the development of the larva within the muscle fibre.[141]

Independently, and in the same year, Virchow conducted some feeding experiments in dogs. He found mature nematodes in the intestine four days after feeding trichinous flesh but failed to observe the migration of the larvae. He did however appreciate that the *Trichinellae* were a species in their own right and formed no part of the life cycle of another species. Thus by the year 1860, as Virchow remarked, " The story of the Trichina therefore is practically closed ". The life cycle was known and the mode of man's infection from pork appreciated. As early as 1848 Joseph Leidy had reported the presence of an entozoon in the muscles of a pig, indistinguishable from that which he had several times found in human muscle and correctly identified from the description of Owen as *Trichinella spiralis.* Leuckart, in his monograph, devoted a chapter to the frequency of trichinella infection in man in various countries pointing out that the incidence was greater in those areas where much pork was eaten. He concluded from his animal experiments that " Trichinae, far from being the harmless guests of man (which it must be remembered they were all this time considered to be) are rather to be counted among his most dreadful enemies ".[142] Leuckart's prediction was dramatically borne out in the same year as he published his monograph. F. A. Zenker reported the results of a study he had made as the result of making a post-mortem examination on the body of a servant girl who had died in Dresden under symptoms simulating, in some respects, typhoid fever with abdominal and muscular pains, oedema and pneumonia. Zenker found numerous *Trichinellae* in the muscles which had not yet become encapsulated and were therefore of recent origin. He made enquiries and found that the girl had assisted with the killing of pigs and the making of sausages a few days before the onset of her illness and she was known to have eaten raw pork during this period. Moreover several other members of the girl's family and the butcher had all been afflicted with a similar disease. Zenker examined one of the hams and some sausages prepared on that occasion and found numerous encapsulated *Trichinellae*. This case was of immense importance from the medical point of view for it proved that man acquired trichinella infection by eating raw pork and that the disease produced, and clearly ascribable to the parasitic infestation, was severe and even fatal.

The work of Leuckart, Virchow and Zenker clearly established the existence of a severe disease of man, trichinosis, which was caused by the entry into the body of a minute nematode worm. Incidentally trichinosis was the first generalized disease of man which was shown to be caused by a microparasite and lent some support to the proposition, at that time barely beginning to be considered, that other fevers might be due to microparasites.

In 1861 Kuchenmeister suggested that a fragment of muscle should be removed from persons with symptoms suggestive of trichinosis using the Middledorpff harpoon, an instrument which had been designed for exploring tumours. In the following year this was done by Professor N. Friedreich of Heidelberg. He had as a patient, a butcher who fell ill about a week after slaughtering some pigs, and the diagnosis of trichinosis was confirmed by the finding of *Trichinellae* in a portion of his biceps muscle.

Once the disease had been recognized there were numerous reports from different towns of quite large outbreaks of the disease. The first of these to be described was in the town of Plauen in Voigtland in 1862. About the middle of March several physicians in Plauen observed cases of a peculiar disease in which marked prostration, extraordinary limb pains, swelling of the face and fever were prominent manifestations. They discussed the cases amongst themselves but remained uncertain of the diagnosis until the answer to the riddle was found, by a Dr. Hagen, who in turning over the pages of a journal, came across an account of Zenker's case and at once recognized the peculiar disease of Plauen as trichinosis. A Dr. Konigsdorfer, on March 28th, excised a small piece of biceps muscle from one of the patients and showed that it contained encysted *Trichinellae*. This little incident indicates a very high standard of general practice in Germany at this date. The general practitioners showed a most praiseworthy keenness, professional co-operation and an awareness of the latest advances as described in the literature. At this late date perhaps the historian may be allowed to compliment the practitioners of Plauen on their fine achievement. In all 30 cases of trichinosis occurred in this outbreak, one of which was fatal.

In October 1863 an even more dramatic outbreak occurred at Heltstadt. It was occasioned by a concatenation of circumstances which led to a large consumption of pork, for in a single week, in the town there occurred the annual market, a pay-day for local miners and smelters and a dinner to celebrate the 50th anniversary of the Battle of Leipzig. A local practitioner, Dr. Rupprecht, saw most of the patients and, although aware of the report of Zenker's case, at first failed to make the diagnosis. However, when many of the cases were traced to a butcher's family and surrounding customers he realized that he was dealing with an outbreak of trichinosis but could not persuade any of his patients to submit to a muscle biopsy. However, shortly after the second week of the epidemic three patients died and the finding of *Trichinellae* in their muscles unquestionably established the diagnosis. Immediately after this many patients consented to undergo muscle biopsy to establish their diagnosis. The remainder of a piece of brawn eaten by six of the patients was found to contain the parasite. Altogether this outbreak consisted of 158 cases, 28 of which were fatal. The fatal cases included an old teacher from a neighbouring village who had actually fought at the battle of Leipzig. A strange chance to have survived the battle only to die of its celebration 50 years later. A great deal was learnt during this outbreak of the clinical features, incubation and epidemiology of the disease. The infected pork had been eaten in a variety of ways with different results. Thus of Dr Rupprecht's 103 cases, 11 had been infected through eating raw pork, of whom four died. Of nine infected by eating smoked sausage four also died. Fourteen were infected by the brawn but only one died and only one person was infected by eating roast pork and he survived.

It was not long before there were reports of outbreaks in many towns in Germany such as Anahlt, Eisleben, Jena, Leipzig, Pastor Göze's Quedlenburg, Strassfurt and Weimar and it was realized that there was a most important public health problem. The various independent states of Germany took different actions. The Royal Provincial Government of Magdeburg published a general warning concerning the dangers of eating raw meat, and the sale of spoiled articles of food, under which heading trichinous meat was considered, was already prohibited by law. Since however it required microscopic examination of the meat to determine whether or not it was infected and no provision was made for this, the law was not particularly helpful. The Government of the Duchy of Brunswick laid down strict rules concerning the inspection of all slaughtered pigs and included provision for the specific examination for *Trichinellae.* Six medical officers of health were appointed to inspect the slaughtered pigs and they were instructed to remove fragments of muscle from the neck, intercostal region and abdomen, moisten them with caustic potash and examine them with a good hand lens. When capsules were not found by this test the pig was considered to be free from trichinae unless it showed signs of enteritis in which case, a proper examination with a microscope magnifying 100 diameters had to be made. It was doubtful how valuable inspection of this type, which had to be paid for by the owner of the pig at the rate of 1/2d. for the first pig and 7d for every other, was in practice. Certainly, during the busy killing season around Christmas and the New Year of 1863/64 when about 10,000 pigs were slaughtered, no cases of trichinosis were found although *Cysticercus cellulosae* was commonly observed.[143]

In Europe microscopic examination of pork specifically for *Trichinellae* was considered an important public health measure although it was appreciated that certain protection could be achieved by proper cooking. Inspection of pork was not carried out in the U.S.A. and so between 1879 and 1881 the governments of Italy, Germany, Portugal, Norway, France, Austria and Hungary prohibited the importation of American pork. In 1891 the Congress of the United States passed an act requiring that pork be inspected for *Trichinellae* and the prohibition of import into Germany was rescinded. However in 1892 a Prussian circular calling for re-inspection of American pork caused some diplomatic difficulties between the two countries.

In Germany trichina inspection became a fetish, there being in 1895 an inspection force of 27,089 in Prussia alone—a number almost as large as the entire regular army of the U.S.A. The costs of inspection however high, could not guarantee freedom from trichinae, but rather gave a false sense of security. In 1906, in the U.S.A. microscopical examination was abandoned. However trichinosis, even in recent times, has been a major public health problem in the U.S.A. since many reports of necropsy series between 1931 and 1942 give an average incidence of trichinosis at autopsy of 16 per cent. Thus we have seen that in less than 30 years, from the first proper observation of the parasite by Paget, the life-cycle, epidemiology, clinical and pathological effects and preventive methods had been worked out and it only remains to mention a few details hitherto not touched upon.

It was clear that the encysted larvae were ingested with the food and hatched out as adults in the small intestine. The larvae there produced as a result of sexual reproduction then migrated to the muscles where they became encysted. The pioneer workers had not however observed the actual route of migration. Leuckart maintained for many years that the larvae penetrated the gut and then migrated via the connective tissue planes to the various parts of the body. Fiedler in 1864 found *Trichinellae* in blood clots within the heart of experimentally infected rabbits and noted both small and large larvae encysted close together in the same muscle. He interpreted these findings as indicating that the larvae were disseminated by the blood stream and at different times. Staubli, in 1905, first demonstrated larvae in the heart blood of living guinea-pigs 7 to 18 days after infection and in 1909, Herrick and Janeway, demonstrated them in the venous blood of a human patient 10 and 12 days after the onset of symptoms. Askanazy at the end of the last century traced the larvae from the lumen of the intestine into the villae, the lymphatics, lacteals and the thoracic duct and so into the blood stream.

An important diagnostic sign of trichinosis was discovered in 1896 by a Johns Hopkins medical student, T. R. Brown. At the Johns Hopkins Hospital it was the duty of the students to carry out the simple clinico-pathological investigations on the patients. Brown found, in a 23-year-old man with trichinosis, that 68 per cent. of the blood leucocytes were eosinophils, a far higher proportion than had been recorded for any other disease. During a four year period following this there were seven cases of trichinosis at the Johns Hopkins with a pronounced eosinophilia and in four of them the diagnosis was actually suggested by the finding of an eosinophilia.[144] Serological investigations were tried as early as 1911 in the diagnosis of trichinosis for in that year Strobel prepared an antigen from trichinous muscle which gave a positive complement test with sera from infected rabbits, guinea-pigs and man. In 1928 Backman introduced an improved antigen with which precipitin and skin sensitivity tests were developed.

Chapter VI

HOOKWORM

THE hookworms have been described as " mankind's worst helminthic pathogen ". It has been estimated that in 1940 there were some 457 million cases in the world out of a total population in the region of 2,166 million. Its frequency is only exceeded by that of *Ascaris* and these two parasites together made up about half of the total helminthiasis of man.[145] The two species of hookworm infesting man are very widely distributed, but are essentially parasites of warmer climates, although, if circumstances are suitable for the transmission of the parasite, outbreaks of infection may occur in countries with a temperate climate. *Ancylostoma duodenale* is found most commonly north of latitude 20 degrees N. whilst the other human species of hookworm, *Necator americanus,* encircles the globe to the south of that line. It is quite ubiquitous in the tropics and its specific name " americanus " has no justification based on geographical distribution.[146]

The clinical manifestations of hookworm infection can be dramatic and consist essentially of severe anaemia, with its attendant signs and symptoms, and intestinal disturbances. The picture is sufficiently characteristic for us to be able to recognize the disease with considerable certainty from ancient descriptions. Thus the clinical picture of hookworm infection was described in the Egyptian Papyrus Ebers of 1550 B.C. The ancient Chinese were familiar with the condition which they named the " able to eat but lazy to work, yellow disease ". Hippocrates described a syndrome including a yellowish colour of the skin, intestinal disturbance and geophagy which was almost certainly due to hookworm infection and Lucretius in the first century B.C. pointed to the skin pallor which was common among miners.[147] The parasite can, however, never have been common in Europe and no advances in the understanding of the condition were made until the eighteenth century. The first modern reports of the clinical condition appeared from the West Indies where the disease was common amongst imported negro slaves. Gradually reports of similar clinical pictures accumulated from different parts of the tropical and subtropical world under a variety of names; " Mal-coeur " of the Antilles, " cachexie aqueuse " in the West Indies, " tuntun " in Colombia and " opilacao " in Brazil.[148] Not unnaturally there was some confusion with the anaemia associated with malaria, the " malarial chlorosis ", but here the morbid anatomists were able to point to a distinction. The enlarged spleen, so characteristic of " malaria chlorosis " was not found in the " cachexie aqueuse ".[149]

Discovery of the Hookworm

The first of the human hookworms to be discovered was the *Ancylostoma duodenale* and indeed almost the whole of the history of the hookworm devolves about this species. It was not until 1888 that Lutz in Brazil noted that his local hookworm differed from the European worm, and it was finally described as a separate species by C. Wardell Stiles of the U.S. Bureau of Animal Industry and named *Necator americanus.*

The discovery of *Ancylostoma duodenale* was reported in 1843 by a Milanese physician, Angelo Dubini. Dubini was born in 1813 in Milan and studied at Pavia where he qualified in 1837. After a couple of years in junior posts in Milan and Pavia he set out for a period of post-graduate study in France, England and Germany. He was an accomplished linguist being familiar with the tongues of all these countries. He devoted himself particularly to the study of morbid anatomy in the museums of the various hospitals he visited and was also introduced to microscopy by David Gruby in Paris. He returned to Milan in 1842 where he obtained a position as assistant in the hospital and remained in hospital and private practice in that city until he retired in 1878 to devote himself to apiculture, on which he was a great authority. He died in 1902 following the fracture of his femur. Dubini's medical interests were wide and included morbid anatomy, rabies and dermatology. He showed considerable courage during a cholera epidemic in 1849, actually catching the disease himself. In all he wrote 54 books or papers only five of which were concerned with parasitology but they constitute his main claim to be remembered. One of his parasitological works was a book of over 500 pages entitled *Entozoographia umana* published in 1850 and which was, in fact, the earliest nineteenth century book to give a complete account of both animal and vegetable parasites of man.

Dubini discovered the hookworm in 1838 in the gut of a peasant dying in the hospital. He recognized that it was a new species but did not associate it with any clinical picture. During the next few years he occasionally came across the same parasite during the course of his autopsies but refrained from publishing any account of the worm as all specimens he had found were females. In 1843 he found many worms in the small intestine of a man dying of pneumonia amongst which were male worms. He had found that the worm was not at all uncommon, being present in approximately 20 per cent. of subjects examined at autopsy. It was apparently associated with a variety of clinical syndromes including cachexia, diarrhoea and oedema but Dubini was too cautious to ascribe to his parasite any causal role. He did, however, give a very full account of the parasite, which he named *Agchylostoma duodenale,* and of the morbid anatomy of the small intestine associated with it. In his *Entozoographia umana* he subsequently changed the name to *Anchylostoma.*[150]

Ancylostoma duodenale was next reported from Egypt by Franz Pruner-Bey in his book *Die Krankheiten des Orients vom Standpunkte der vergleichenden Nosologie betrachtet* published in 1847. Franz Pruner was born in Munich in 1808. Soon after graduation, in 1830, he went for a period of post-graduate study to Paris and then went to Egypt to investigate an outbreak of plague. He had always wanted to travel in the East and he accepted a succession of positions under the Egyptian government being, in 1839, made personal physician to Abbas-Pasha and given the title of Bey. He wrote books on plague and cholera as well as his textbook on tropical diseases. Pruner became particularly interested in anthropology and when he returned to Europe, for health reasons, after nearly 30 years in Egypt, he continued these studies in Paris. However with the outbreak of the Franco-Prussian War he was compelled to leave Paris and went to Pisa where he died in 1882.[151] He bequeathed his personal fortune to the University of Munich for the assistance of poor students. It was not, however, until the work of Griesinger and Bilharz, about 1853, that a specific pathological effect, severe anaemia, was shown to be due to infestation with *Ancylostoma duodenale*. The story of Bilharz's life is more appropriately dealt with in connection with his most important discovery of the *Schistosoma haematobium* but it should be noted that he was associated with this important work on ancylostomiasis. Wilhelm Griesinger was born in Stuttgart in 1817, the son of a hospital administrator. He studied medicine at Tübingen and Zürich. On qualification he settled in practice in Friedrichshafen but soon obtained a post as an assistant in a mental hospital. Mental disease became his main interest and he made such good use of his opportunities that, in 1845, he was able to publish a book on the subject. After work for some time in Stuttgart and Tübingen he was made director of a polyclinic in Kiel in 1849 but, almost immediately, was compelled to leave for political reasons. He went to Egypt as head of the Cairo Medical School and physician to the Khedive. Griesinger spent but three years in Egypt, returning to Stuttgart in 1852, because of ill-health. His parasitological work was accomplished during this brief sojourn in Egypt. On his return to Germany he wrote a comprehensive article on the diseases prevalent in Egypt which contains his observations on parasites. His subsequent career was one of distinction in psychiatry. He became director of the psychiatric and neurological service at the Charité Hospital, Berlin, in 1865, founded the "Archiv für Psychiatrie and Nerven Krankheiten ", and died of appendicitis in 1868.[152]

According to Davaine, Griesinger, although suggesting that ancylostoma were the cause of Egyptian chlorosis by no means satisfactorily proved the point. Indeed it was only at the last autopsy he attended, just before his return to Europe, that he found ancylostoma plus a considerable quantity of blood in the duodenum. Thus Davaine, writing in 1860, considered that more work was needed to be done to establish this most important point. Indeed Griesinger's views were not generally accepted until they were confirmed by Wucherer in Brazil.[153]

In 1866 Wucherer was called to see a negro slave belonging to the Benedictine Monastery at Bahia. Clinically he was suffering from severe " hypoaemia ". Wucherer returned home to look up the literature on the subject and in Hirsch's *Geologico-Medical Reports* found an account of Griesinger's observations in Egypt and immediately recognized his " hypoaemia " as identical with " Egyptian chlorosis ". On returning to the monastery next day he found his patient had died. After a good deal of opposition from the Benedictine monks he obtained permission to make a limited post-mortem examination. He was able to open the abdomen only but there, in the duodenum, he found the ancylostoma. As soon as he could he performed post-mortem examinations upon the bodies of 20 miserably poor patients at the General Infirmary of Bahia. Five of these patients had typical hypoaemia and in all of these he found the parasite. Wucherer sent specimens of the parasite to Griesinger who confirmed their identity with the ancylostoma and also to London to a Doctor Weber who showed them to Cobbold and demonstrated them at a meeting of the Pathological Society of London. He also published an account of his observations in a local medical journal and in a German journal.[154] Wucherer's accurate and well publicized observations effectively drew attention to the ancylostoma as an important cause of anaemia, particularly in the tropics, and numerous other writers rapidly verified his observations.

In Europe, Grassi showed, in 1878, that infestation could be readily diagnosed by the microscopical examination of faeces when characteristic eggs containing larvae would be found. The importance of ancylostoma infection was impressed upon the medical profession of Europe in 1880 during the construction of the St Gotthard tunnel between Italy and Switzerland when there was a severe outbreak of anaemia amongst the Italian miners employed on the work. Perroncito, professor of pathology at Turin, demonstrated that the anaemia was due to ancylostoma infestation. When the work on the tunnel was completed the workers dispersed all over Europe and wherever they worked in mines ancylostomiasis became common.

So serious had the problem become in German mines by 1903 that measures had to be taken to combat the disease. In that year some 13 per cent. of miners were infested. It was therefore decided that all new miners should have their faeces examined microscopically and any found infected were excluded from the mine. Adequate sanitation was provided and known cases treated with anthelmintics. These measures were largely successful so that by 1914 the incidence of infection in German miners was only 0·17 per cent. In the Sicilian sulphur mines, where no prophylactic measures had been taken, the incidence of infection had reached 50 per cent. by 1912.[155]

In England the problem never seems to have been widespread but ancylostomiasis certainly occurred as J. S. Haldane and A. E. Boycott found in Cornwall. Haldane had been asked by the Home Secretary to investigate the ventilation in Cornish mines and it was whilst engaged upon this work that he stumbled on the condition of ancylostomiasis. Haldane and Boycott found that cases of anaemia amongst miners had first been noticed about 1897 and during that year 29 patients were admitted to hospital for this cause. Of all known cases of anaemia amongst miners 61 per cent. came from the single mine at Dolcoath. The two workers established that the anaemia was due to ancylostomiasis and showed that examination of blood for eosinophilia was a valuable diagnostic procedure. They investigated hygienic conditions in the mine, noted that there were no lavatories underground and faecal contamination of the mine was widespread and that all samples of faeces examined contained the eggs of the ancylostoma. Conditions in the mine were damp and muddy and faecal contaminated mud was freely distributed on rungs of ladders, water casks, etc.[156]

Until the end of the nineteenth century it was believed that hookworm spread from man to man by means of the worm's eggs. The assumption was not unnatural and was indeed supported by the work of Leuckart on the hookworm of the dog and by feeding experiments in human subjects carried out by Leichtenstern in 1886. The latter worker had been able to infect human subjects by feeding fully developed eggs but not the hatched out larvae. He found that within about a month his subjects were passing hookworm eggs in their faeces.[157]

Here the matter rested until the work of Arthur Looss, around the turn of the century, demonstrated the true mode of transmission of the hookworm. Looss, a German citizen, was born in 1861 and studied at Leipzig under Leuckart. He was early attracted to the study of parasitology, publishing a small book on the general aspects of the subject and its history in 1892 and throughout his life was a prolific writer on parasitology. In 1896 he settled in Egypt because of the excellent opportunities that country afforded for the study of parasitology. Here he passed the most fruitful years of his working life and by his discoveries, his experimental methods and writings infused new life into the whole science of helminthology. On the outbreak of the First World War in 1914 he was, on account of his nationality, expelled from Egypt. He served in the German Army and died in 1923.

In 1898 whilst dropping culture of ancylostoma larvae into the mouths of guinea-pigs Looss accidentally allowed some of the material to fall onto his hand. He noticed that it produced an itching sensation and erythema of the skin. He repeated the observation and wondered if natural infection occurred in this way. He examined samples of his own faeces at intervals thereafter and in due course found that he was excreting hookworm eggs. His next experiment was to put drops of ancylostoma larvae culture on the skin of the leg of an Egyptian boy an hour before it was due to be amputated. Subsequent sections of the area of skin showed, under the microscope, the larvae in the process of penetrating the skin. He later extended his work to dogs and showed that the larvae of *Ancylostoma caninum* also passed through the skin. These results he first reported in a series of papers and in 1911 he published a monograph on the subject.[158]

Some early attempts to confirm the observation of Looss failed. Thus Boycott and Haldane reported that " one of us " had tried to infect himself by smearing faecal cultures of ancylostoma on the skin without success and Pieri, working in Grassi's laboratory, had but partial success.[159] However in 1902 C. A. Bentley, a medical officer on an Assam tea plantation, reported the results of a beautiful piece of work which strongly supported the view that ancylostoma larvae penetrated the intact skin of man. His paper deserves to be recalled not only on account of its importance in connection with the subject at hand but as yet another example of good work done by an individual in isolation and in primitive conditions. Bentley's paper was entitled " on the causal relationship between ' ground itch ' or pani-ghao and the presence of the larvae of *Ankylostoma duodenale* in the soil ". " Ground itch " was common amongst the coolies of the tea plantation and Bentley, having read a report that it was caused by a type of acarus, resolved to check the statement. He applied some soil taken from near the coolies' lines to the skin of his own arm and developed typical ground itch. However, careful microscopy failed to reveal any acari. The soil did contain numerous ancylostoma larvae, minute leeches, earthworms, rotifers as well as protozoa, fungi and bacteria. Bentley showed that it must be some living organism in the soil which caused the itch since sterilized soil was innocuous. Next he examined microscopically scrapings taken from the skin over typical ground itch lesions and found ancylostoma larvae and empty larvae sheaths. He would have liked to have made a histological study of the lesions but " not having a microtome or other apparatus necessary for preparing sections, it was impossible to make this part of the investigation as complete as could have been wished ". He therefore adopted an experimental approach. He took two samples of soil and contaminated one with faeces containing ancylostoma larvae and the other with normal faeces. A portion of each sample was then dried for eight hours and then some of each sample was applied to the wrists and held in place by a bandage. Typical ground itch lesions developed only under the sample containing living ancylostoma larvae.[160]

Thus it became established that there were two possible modes of infection by the hookworm; by the penetration of the larvae into the skin and by the ingestion of mature eggs. A consideration of the hygienic conditions under which hookworm infection occurred made it clear that the former method, penetration of the skin by the larvae, was likely to be the most important. In primitive tropical communities people went about barefoot and made no attempt to dispose of faeces in a hygienic manner.

Knowledge of the life-history of the parasite clearly pointed the way to prevention of hookworm disease and in 1913 the Sanitary Commission of the Rockefeller Foundation decided to tackle the problem. They chose Porto Rico as the initial site of their activities. Here it was estimated that one-third of all deaths were due to hookworm infestation. The commission's method was to take an area, map it, examine all the residents, treat any cases of hookworm infestation with anthelmintics, provide proper latrines and persuade the people to use them—the most difficult part of the task. In 1915 the work of the Rockefeller Commission was merged with that of the International Health Board and their activities extended from Porto Rico to tropical countries all over the world including some southern states of the U.S.A. where the disease was an important problem. Their work was of the greatest importance not only in stamping out, or at least reducing, the incidence of hookworm disease but also in providing a great impetus to hygiene in general and, in stressing the hygienic disposal of human faeces, contributed to the control of many other diseases.

The history of the drug treatment of hookworm infestation has been dealt with by Scott and will be but briefly alluded to. The original anthelmintics used in the treatment of other worm infestations were found to be of little use. Following experimental work by Perroncito and clinical trials by Bozzolo about 1880, thymol, a phenolic compound obtained from the aromatic oils of *Thymus vulgaris,* was found to be useful. It was, however, unpleasant to take and rather toxic. Oil of chenopodium, introduced in 1915, was an improvement and later introductions, more effective and less toxic, have been carbon tetrachloride, tetrachloroethylene and hexylresorcinol.[161]

Chapter VII

WUCHERERIA BANCROFTI

CONDITIONS suitable for the spread of this parasite amongst man occur over a wide belt of the earth's surface in tropical and subtropical countries. The belt extends roughly from 40° N. to 35° S. of the equator. Its European stations are limited to parts of Hungary and Turkey but it is widespread along the southern shore of the Mediterranean Sea, in Arabia, India, Malaya and South China. The Pacific islands are particularly heavily infested areas and in the New World it is endemic in Panama, Colombia, Venezuela and Brazil almost as far south as the borders of Argentina. Until recently there was a focus of infestation near Charleston, S. Carolina.

The incidence of infection with *Wuchereria bancrofti* has been, and in many of the areas named still is, extremely high but disease occurs in only a minority of infected persons. The manifestations of the disease are various but undoubtedly the most striking is the condition known as elephantiasis. The word elephantiasis has however been used to describe two distinct clinical conditions. The ancient Greek and Roman writers used the term to describe a condition in which the skin was thickened and fissured like the hide of an elephant and from their full accounts of the condition the cases referred to were undoubtedly leprosy. Aretaeus prefaces his account of the condition with a long description of the elephant but the disease he described was leprosy.[162] The Arabian writers, Avicenna and Avenzoar, who no doubt had experience of true elephantiasis made a distinction under this heading into cases of " lepra " and " elephants " reserving the latter name for a disease characterized by a leg much swollen, like that of an elephant.[163] For a thousand years no new knowledge of elephantiasis or the other manifestations of *Wuchereria bancrofti* infection was gained although the condition was known, casually, to Rabelais and Blanchard in the sixteenth century.

Two other manifestations of *W. bancrofti* infection beside elephantiasis are hydrocoele and chyluria and it was in connection with these two conditions that the parasite was first described. Hydrocoele is a common condition in temperate climates and only an occasional case imported from the tropics is due to *Wuchereria* infection. Chyluria is however an uncommon condition and although it can be caused by agents other than *Wuchereria bancrofti,* the latter is by far the commonest cause even in temperate climates.

The clinical syndrome of chyluria was recognized in the early nineteenth century and a good account of it was given by William Prout in his book *On the Nature and Treatment of Stomach and Renal Diseases* published in 1848 in which he summarized all that was known of the condition. He had, in his own practice, seen 14 cases of chyluria. The aetiology was unknown to him but he appreciated that it was associated with residence in hot climates, no less than eight of his cases being in natives or those who had resided many years in the East or West Indies. He further noted that the general health was less disturbed than might be expected and that the condition might continue for many years. He was also able to examine the kidneys of one case at autopsy and found them perfectly healthy. The parasite actually responsible for some cases of tropical hydrocoele, chyluria and elephantiasis or rather its embryo was first seen by Demarquay in Paris in 1863 when he examined under the microscope the hydrocoele fluid of a patient from Havana and found the microfilariae.[164]

In 1866 O. Wucherer, of German ancestry but born in Portugal, who practised in Bahia, Brazil, was examining the urine of a patient with chyluria, actually looking for Bilharzia parasites which had been found to be the cause of the endemic haematuria of Egypt, when he noted the presence of " filarial worms ". He immediately obtained a fresh specimen of urine, for nematodes are common free living organisms which might have been contaminating it, and confirmed the presence of the organisms. He did not however immediately publish his findings but searched patiently for further cases of infestation with this parasite. During the next two years he found several more cases and published an account of them in the *Bahia Medical Gazette* in

December 1868. This journal had but a limited circulation and his observations went virtually unknown throughout the world.

During the next few years a number of people in different parts of the world independently saw the embryo filariae in the urine of patients with chyluria, for example, T. R. Lewis in Calcutta in 1870, M. Robin in Réunion in 1872 and even T. S. Cobbold in London in 1870. Cobbold, who was very familiar with the world literature on helminthology, was at that time unaware of Wucherer's publication.[165] Timothy Richard Lewis was born in Pembrokeshire in 1841. We do not know what determined him upon a medical career but at the age of 15 he was apprenticed to a local practitioner. He enjoyed a varied medical education. At the age of 19 he came up to London to study at University College, where he obtained a silver medal for clinical medicine; later at the German Hospital he acquired an excellent knowledge of that language. He finally graduated from Aberdeen in 1867. He decided to enter the Army Medical Department and in 1868 passed into the Army Medical School top of the list. There he did exceptionally well and at the end of his term was sent with D. D. Cunningham to Germany specially to learn about the fungus theory of the aetiology of cholera. This was, of course, before bacteria had been shown to play any part in pathological processes but there was a considerable body of opinion supporting the role of fungi in disease. Fungi had indeed been shown to be the cause of ringworm in man and various diseases of plants and animals, and there were those who claimed that they were also responsible for a number of generalized fevers of man, particularly cholera. Chief amongst these was Professor Hallier at Jena whom they visited. They also called on Professor Pettenkofer at Munich where he had recently founded the first scientific institute of hygiene in the world. After a visit lasting about three months Lewis and Cunningham sailed for India and reached Calcutta early in 1869. Almost immediately they were attached for special duties to the Sanitary Commissioner of the Government of India, and Lewis, although an army medical officer, appears to have spent his whole career in researches related to that Commission. His investigations of cholera yielded no positive results but as will be seen set him on the track of his important work on filaria. He contributed to a great variety of subjects during a tour of nearly 14 years in India. In 1884 he accepted the post of assistant professor at Netley where he introduced, for the first time, a course in practical bacteriology. In 1884 he went to Marseilles to try to confirm Koch's discovery of the comma-bacillus of cholera which however he failed to do. In 1886 he was recommended for the Fellowship of the Royal Society but before he could receive this honour he was suddenly struck down with pneumonia and died at the age of 44 years.[166]

Lewis discovered the embryo filaria accidentally when investigating the alvine discharges of cholera patients. Writing of the urine in a case of chyluria he explained that "As the colour so closely resembled many rice-water stools, I carefully examined it, and was repaid in a way I had not anticipated". He saw, described and figured the "embryos of a round worm". He hoped that "perhaps this fact may help to throw some light on a very obscure disease" and was well aware that all he had seen were the embryos and not the adult worm. He wrote "as the mature worm still retains a hold on his victim, being perhaps safely lodged in the kidney, and not having seen an embryo of this kind before, nor yet a drawing, I must leave it to a more experienced helminthologist to decide to what species of nematode it belongs".[167] Lewis published his discoveries, in a manner hardly less obscure than had Wucherer, in the annual reports of the Sanitary Commissioner. Again, quite by chance, in 1872, whilst examining the blood of an Indian with diarrhoea, he observed the same embryos, immediately recognizing them as identical to those he had seen in chylous urine two years previously. He sent a slide of them to Professor Parkes at Netley who showed it to George Busk who said the worms were filariae. Lewis published an account of the discovery as an appendix to the *Report of the Sanitary Commissioner to the Government of India.* From this time on he paid particular attention to the subject publishing, in 1874, in the *Indian Annals of Medical Science,* a full account of his experience in a paper entitled "On a Haematozoon in Human Blood and its Relation to Chylous Urine and other Diseases". In this paper he stated that he had found the embryos in blood, urine or both in 20 patients, including five Europeans. He described the anatomy of the embryos and made out that it was "enveloped in an extremely delicate tube, closed at both ends" and considered that the natural home of the embryos was the blood. He postulated that the chyluria was due to blockage of the lymphatic vessels by the parasites with subsequent dilatation and rupture of lymphatic vessels in the walls of the renal tract. Some of the patients he described suffered from hydrocoeles or elephantiasis but he made no special comment about this. By a curious chance, when visiting the government printing press, he found his original patient in whose chylous urine he had first discovered the filariae, actually setting up the type for his paper and had the satisfaction, but only after prolonged search, of finding the embryos in his blood also.

We now have to consider the work of one whose work on filarial disease not only added knowledge of fundamental importance to the subject but greatly enlarged our view of parasitology by demonstrating that insects might act as vectors for parasites. The man alluded to is, of course, Patrick Manson. Born in Aberdeenshire, in 1844, of a middle class family, he was led by a taste for natural history to take up medicine as a career. He was studious but not a brilliant scholar and entered Aberdeen University in 1860. He passed his final examinations by the age of 20 and being too young to take his degree went up to London for a few months' further study. His first appointment as a doctor in this country was a period of seven months spent as medical officer in a Durham mental hospital. Here he conducted his own necropsies upon which he was able to base a paper on aneurysm of the internal carotid artery. This same paper served as his thesis for the M.D. degree which was awarded to him in the same year, 1866, an index of the low standards required at that time rather than any demonstration of exceptional capacity in Manson.[168] He then obtained a post as a medical officer in the Chinese Imperial Maritime Customs Service. This service which was run by the British under an inspector general stationed at Peking, maintained a staff of about 20 British medical officers distributed between 17 treaty ports along the Chinese coast and neighbouring islands, the senior medical officer in charge being a Dr. R. A. Jamieson stationed at Shanghai. Manson's first appointment was to the port of Takao in Formosa where he arrived in June 1866. The European community in Takao amounted to some 17 souls and Manson's duties consisted of medical inspections of ships calling at

Takao, running the local missionary hospital and carrying on his private practice. His duties allowed him ample leisure for sport and travel about the interesting countryside where he observed everything with the eyes of a naturalist, recording his observations in a journal. The life was healthy and prosperous, so that within three years he was able to repay his father the £700 spent on his medical education. Manson spent nearly five years in Takao and then in 1871 was posted to Amoy close to the mainland of China. This was a much larger port and boasted a European population of about 150, but Manson's life, with respect to his duties and recreations, was very similar to what it had been at Takao. Manson threw himself into his work with his accustomed energy. The native mission hospital opened a wide field for observation of diseases almost entirely unknown to western medical services. Manson was not alone in realizing the wonderful opportunities there were for research, despite the professional isolation, in the Chinese Customs Medical Service. In 1870, the inspector-general, Robert Hart sent round a circular in which he wrote that "It has been suggested to me that it would be well to take advantage of the circumstances in which the customs establishment is placed to procure information with regard to disease amongst foreigners and natives in China . . ." and he therefore ordered that there should be published, by each medical officer for his respective area, half-yearly reports in the *Customs Gazette*. The first Customs medical gazette was published in 1871 and from the first contained much material of the greatest interest. The reports were never solely of a statistical nature. Detailed case reports, accounts of epidemics (such as Manson's account of an outbreak of dengue fever with illustrative temperature charts, published in 1872), sanitary conditions and habits of the natives were recorded. The only criticism which can be levelled against this excellent medical publication being that it diverted important papers from journals with a wider circulation and as a result much good work lay virtually buried.[169]

Manson's work was, of course, general practice in its broadest sense. The native hospital catered for over 100 surgical operations a year. It was his surgical practice which was to lead Manson to his great work on the filaria parasites. Elephantiasis in its various manifestations was one of the commonest and most disabling conditions he was called upon to treat. Initially his interest in this condition was that of a surgeon. Unaided he devised an operation for the safe removal of these vast scrotal tumours and gradually broke down native prejudice with respect to surgery. He described in some early numbers of Customs medical reports a variant of scrotal elephantiasis, in which lymphatic varices rather than diffuse thickening of the tissues predominated, under the name of "lymph scrotum", a term he coined himself having failed to find any description of the condition in the textbooks. It was therefore natural that when spending the year of 1875 on leave in England he should endeavour to find out all he could about this common problem of elephantiasis and related conditions. Men with practical knowledge of the subject he could not, of course, find but some useful literature he was able to discover in the reading room of the British Museum. Here he came across textbooks, and particularly Indian journals, which helped him to formulate a working hypothesis relating to the whole pathology of elephantiasis. He found that his condition of "lymph scrotum" had already been described in India in 1854 and that in important papers in 1861 and 1862, Vandyke Carter had discussed its pathology and relation to elephantiasis. He also came across the papers of Lewis "On a Haematozoon in Human Blood" 1872, "On a Haematozoon in Human Blood and its Relation to Chyluria and Other Diseases" 1874 and "The Pathological Significance of Nematode Haematozoa" 1874. These papers added greatly to his knowledge of the aetiology and pathology of elephantiasis and on his return to China he published in the Customs medical reports "a short résumé of what I have been able to glean" and his conclusions based on his own experience. His object in this paper was to bring evidence to establish, as he wrote, "first, the generic identity of lymph scrotum and the ordinary form of elephantiasis; second, the generic identity of elephantiasis and tropical chyluria; third, I will bring forward evidence to support the inference that these three diseases acknowledge the same aetiological cause; and, lastly, this cause I hope to show is the filaria of Lewis".

Although none of these propositions could be said to be entirely original they had been little more than hinted at, had never been so clearly stated and about them there was no general agreement. Reasoning from the account of the pathological effects of the canine filaria, *F. immitis,* given by Lewis, he stated, " if such and so great damage is done by the canine nematode to its favourite nidus, we may infer that something similar occurs in the case of the human subject. We do not as yet know the seat of the parent parasite but I suppose it to be on or in the lymphatics, the receptaculum chyli, or the thoracic duct, or some blood vessel in the neighbourhood of these ". " Post-mortem evidence ", he continued, " is still wanting, and it is a matter for regret that the prejudices of the Chinese deny us the chance of obtaining it here. However, from India, where the natives are not so averse to their dead being dissected, we may hope, ere long, to have the remaining difficulties and obscurities cleared up ".[170] Manson himself did his best to verify his hypothesis as to the site of the adult nematode. On one occasion he concluded a bargain with a dying Chinaman's wife that, for the sum of 200 dollars, he should, after the man's death, be allowed to carry out an autopsy. He and his brother began their examination in an exceedingly hot and ill-lit room where the body lay. Before they had completed their work a mob gathered outside wanting to know what the " foreign devils " were doing and the two brothers had to run for their lives.[171] On only one occasion was he able to complete an autopsy on the body of a Chinaman and this had to be done in the gruesome surroundings of a Chinese cemetery at dead of night by the light of a dimly burning lantern. It is hardly surprising under the circumstances, that Manson was not the first to identify the adult filaria.[172]

The first to find the adult worm was Joseph Bancroft of Brisbane. His attention had been directed to filaria in 1876 when he discovered the embryos in blood. He did not know what they were and so sent specimens to his old teacher, Dr. Roberts of Manchester, who forwarded them to Cobbold. Cobbold recognized them for what they were and wrote to Bancroft instructing him to search for the parent worm. This he discovered in a surprisingly short time, by December 1876 in fact, in a lymphatic abscess of the arm.[173] In April 1877 he wrote to Cobbold " I have laboured hard to find the parental form of the parasite, and am glad to tell you that I have now obtained five specimens of the worm, which are waiting to be forwarded by a trustworthy messenger ". Bancroft had meanwhile observed about 20 cases of filariasis and was of the opinion that they caused chyluria, haematuria, lymphatic abscesses and some hydrocoeles. He made the point that there were no cases of true elephantiasis in Australia but wrote, " I am of the opinion that the parasitic nature of the same will be established ". Cobbold published a short account of Bancroft's discovery in the *Lancet* in July 1877.[174]

In August the same year Lewis's efforts to find the adult worm were rewarded. He found the worm in a case of scrotal elephantiasis and published his account in the *Lancet* in September 1877.[175] Cobbold gave a full description of the material which Bancroft had sent to him in the same journal in October.[176] Manson did not finally discover the adult filaria for a further five years when he found it in the dilated lymphatics of a case of lymph scrotum.[177]

It is curious that Bancroft, who commenced his investigations so long after Lewis and even Manson, should have so rapidly succeeded in discovering the adult parasite. Perhaps native prejudice against both surgery and post-mortem examinations in India and China hampered the two latter workers. Cobbold proposed naming the parasite *Filaria bancrofti*. A few months later one of Wucherer's fellow practitioners from Bahia wrote to the *Lancet* saying that it would have been but just for Wucherer's name to be associated with the parasite and this has now come to pass, the modern name for this parasite being *Wuchereria bancrofti*.[178] Cobbold wrote, in apportioning credit, " In short the helminthologist of the future, when dealing with the question of the discovery of this entozoon, will find himself obliged to bracket the names of four distinguished observers together. Would he seek to be disinterestedly just, he must also award more or less conspicuous merit to the several other workers whose names will naturally be read between the lines that record the discoveries of Wucherer, Lewis, Bancroft and Manson ".[179]

Thus at the end of 1877 the work of these four observers had established the relationship between the various clinical conditions, chyluria, lymph scrotum and elephantiasis and shown that they all depended upon lymphatic obstruction brought about by the presence of the adult parasite. It had also been shown that infected patients usually had embryo filaria in their blood stream. The aetiology of the elephantiasis group of diseases was therefore established but nothing was known of its epidemiology. To the problem of how filaria got into the human body Manson now addressed himself with results of fundamental importance to parasitology as a whole. Manson's interest in the filaria was by now thoroughly aroused and he lost no opportunity of studying them. Early in 1877 he published, again in the *Custom's Gazette,* a review article entitled "Report on Haematozoa" written, as he said: "as I presume that, like myself, most medical practitioners in China do not possess works on the subject, and have no opportunity of consulting them, my observations may be of some value notwithstanding their crudeness". He described two species of filaria in dogs: *Filaria immitis* in which the adult worm lived in the right side of the heart, the embryos circulating in the blood. This worm he was familiar with as he was not infrequently asked to make a post-mortem examination on dogs which had died suddenly and were suspected of being poisoned. The commonest cause of such sudden death was the plugging of the pulmonary artery by the adult worms. Another canine species he described as *Filaria sanguinolenta,* the adult of which was found in the wall of the oesophagus, stomach or thoracic aorta where it caused the production of small nodular tumours. The life-cycle of both these parasites was completely unknown but he raised the possibility of the embryo being somehow swallowed.

Turning to what was generally known at the time as *Filaria sanguinis hominis* (*W. bancrofti*) he suggested that they too, by analogy with *F. sanguinolenta* might be the cause of a common type of oesophageal tumour in man. Referring to a recent patient, however, he was able to write: "I have lately found in the blood of a patient who came to me for the removal of an elephantiasis scroti, numerous specimens of embryo filaria. I am thus enabled to state positively that elephantiasis Arabum is a parasitic disease, and to establish on solid and incontrovertible grounds, what in a former report I conjectured was the true pathology of this puzzling affection". He had examined the blood of 190 Chinese for the presence of filaria embryos. The cases were drawn from hospital patients, their relatives and friends being an unselected group except for their willingness to have their fingers pricked. He found the embryos 15 times. Of these only three had scrotal elephantiasis or lymph scrotum. Seven others had a variety of disabilites but five were in perfect health. Later in the year he published another paper, "Further observations on *Filaria sanguinis hominis*". He reported the results of a systematic survey of the blood of as many Chinese as possible. Out of 670, 62, or more than 9 per cent., harboured embryos. He tried to correlate the presence of the parasites with various factors and found that the incidence increased with increasing age, until, in patients over 70, one in three were affected. There seemed to be little difference in sex incidence but social prejudice had limited his examinations of females to a very small number. He made an elaborate table of occupations comparing the incidence in different trades but with the exception of sailors (in whom there were no cases out of 22 examined) all occupations seemed equally affected. With regard to the relation between the presence of embryos and disease he found that of persons with elephantiasis, lymph scrotum, chyluria and enlarged glands in the groin 36 out of 63 harboured filariae. This figure, when he had applied a correction factor allowing for not finding embryos in all cases in which they were present, gave an incidence of 1 in 1·1 cases. A comparable corrected rate for healthy Chinese gave an incidence of 1 in 12. All these observations were useful work but the section of the paper devoted to his views on the development of the embryos constitutes the classic part of the publication and represents Manson's most original contribution to medical science.

What happened to the circulating embryos was completely unknown. It seemed hardly likely that they could all develop into adult worms in the same host because they were so numerous. It was known that they were sometimes passed in the urine. Lewis had reported finding them in tears and it was possible that, having effected an exit from the human body in this way, they invaded another small host animal which was in turn swallowed by man. Manson cautiously commented, "This is the history of many entozoa, but I have evidence to adduce that, if it be one way in which *Filaria sanguinis hominis* is nursed, it is not the only way, and therefore probably not the way at all". He went on: "It occurred to me that as the first step in the history of the haematozoon was in the blood, the next might happen in an animal who fed on that fluid. To test this idea I procured mosquitoes that fed on the patient Hinloo's blood, and examining the expressed contents of their abdomens from day to day with the microscope, I found that my idea was correct, and that the haematozoon which entered the mosquito, a simple structureless animal, left it, after passing through a series of highly interesting metamorphoses, much increased in size, possessing an alimentary canal, and being otherwise suited for an independent existence ". Thus simply did Manson announce his great discovery. He described his technique for infecting mosquitoes and the developmental changes in the embryos in detail. He noted that blood in the mosquito's stomach contained far more embryos than did blood taken direct from man, and realized that there must be some selective mechanism, further evidence that the mosquito was the normal intermediate host.

But with regard to the further development of the filariae he wrote: " There can be little doubt as to the subsequent history of the filaria; or that escaping into the water in which the mosquito died, it is through the medium of this fluid brought into contact with the tissues of man, and then either piercing the integuments, or what is more probable, being swallowed, it works its way through the alimentary canal to its final resting place ".

The practical importance of his discovery he appreciated immediately: " From the fact of the disease depending on so tangible a link as the mosquito, it is quite possible to prevent its spread, if not to secure its extermination ". He suggested that the dependence of the parasite on the mosquito very beautifully accounted for the geographical distribution of the disease, regarding mosquitoes as essentially tropical insects and being quite unaware of their world-wide occurrence.[180] However few people can have had access to the obscure journal in which Manson published his distinguished observations and the effective publication of his work was delayed until March 1878 when Cobbold communicated it to the Linnean Society on Manson's behalf.

In 1878 Lewis confirmed Manson's discovery of the development of the embryos in mosquitoes, repeating the latter's work most carefully. He found that 14 per cent. of mosquitoes caught randomly contained developing embryos and that in one house where all the mosquitoes caught contained embryos a filarious person was found in perfect health. Lewis kept his infected mosquitoes in covered test-tubes containing a little water, examining them at intervals until death. At that time he noted, " Either no filariae were found in its body, or if present they were dead, and careful examination of the water invariably yielded negative results in my hands. It would seem that the larvae had perished. As the quantity of water used was so small, it is hardly possible, had filariae in any stage of growth been present, that they could have so completely escaped observation ".[181] Thus doubt was immediately cast on Manson's theory as to how the embryos entered the human body. Furthermore in 1883 an anonymous reviewer of Manson's work, in the *Veterinarian* actually suggested that the full grown larvae were " deposited by the mosquito in the act of biting ". Manson may have been led astray by trusting a book on natural history which stated that mosquitoes were ephemeral animals which died in water once their eggs were laid whereas in fact, they can live for several weeks.[182]

Manson had, however, yet one more most interesting observation to make on the natural history of filariae. He had frequently noticed that in patients whose blood he knew to be infested with filariae the embryos sometimes could not be found. He therefore trained two Chinese assistants to make regular examinations of the blood of a filarious patient throughout the whole 24 hours of the day and was struck by the fact that the daytime observer found filaria embryos far less frequently than the night-time observer. He immediately grasped the significance of this observation which he described in a letter to Cobbold written in June 1879, accompanying specimens of infected mosquitoes and a lymph scrotum with case report. He wrote " this observation illustrates well a new fact in the history of filaria. The young escape into the circulation at regular intervals of twenty-four hours, the discharge commencing soon after sunset and continuing till near midnight, from which time till the following noon their numbers gradually decrease. By 2 or 4 o'clock till 6 they are nearly completely absent. This is a striking and most suggestive fact, and in connection with it one might be tempted to speculate on the causes of the periodicity of malarial fevers. It is marvellous how nature has adapted the habits of the filariae to those of the mosquito. The embryos are in the blood just at the time the mosquito selects for feeding ".[183]

When Cobbold announced this discovery at a scientific meeting in London " it was received with bushels of chaff, a Gratiano present displaying one of his few grains of wit in the question 'whether the filariae carry watches' ". However, Manson's observation was soon confirmed by several workers, even by one in London. For in 1881 Dr Stephen Mackenzie, at that time an assistant physician to the London Hospital, presented a case of a filaria infected soldier to the Pathological Society on whom he had not only confirmed the periodicity of the embryos in the blood but showed that the periodicity could be reversed by making the subject sleep during the day and keeping him awake during the night.[184]

Manson soon confirmed Mackenzie's observation and although he recognized that the periodicity had a teleological explanation in the habits of the mosquito he went to considerable trouble to try and discover the mechanism behind the phenomenon. He showed that the appearance and disappearance of the embryos in the blood was not dependent upon intermittent production by the parent worm. Lymph oozing from a lymph scrotum and chylous urine was equally charged with embryos throughout the whole day. He showed that keeping a man in the dark during the day made no difference to the normal periodicity of the embryos and it appeared that periodicity was not related to any particular meteorological factors. Although anxious to do further work altering the conditions of the filarious subject and observing the effect on the periodicity of the embryos " unfortunately the man, Tin, who was the subject of the observation . . . had had enough of it."[185]

It was not until 1897 when he was working in London that he discovered what happened to the embryos during the day when they were absent from the peripheral blood. A filarious patient whom he had been studying in the Charing Cross Hospital committed suicide by taking prussic acid at 8.30 a.m. when there were no embryos in the peripheral blood. At autopsy the capillaries of the lungs were found to be crowded with filaria embryos.[186] The final step in the life cycle of the filaria, the entry of the mature embryos into man remained unknown for over 20 years after Manson's original discovery of the mosquito as the intermediate host. During that time the world was content to accept Manson's hypothesis that the embryos were liberated into water at the death of the mosquito and after a period of free-living existence were swallowed by man.

Doubt was first cast on this theory in 1899 by Thomas Bancroft, son of the Joseph Bancroft after whom the parasite was named. He developed a technique for keeping mosquitoes alive in captivity for much longer periods by feeding them on bananas. He was thus able to follow the embryos much longer and showed that the mature embryos did not survive for long in water.[187] He postulated that the embryos might be swallowed inside a mosquito, a somewhat improbable event, or, alternatively, that they might re-enter the oesophagus of the mosquito and creep along into human tissues when the mosquito was taking its blood meal. Bancroft sent a supply of *Filaria* infected mosquitoes preserved in glycerine to Manson in London. Manson had working with him a young Scottish doctor, George Low, who had been qualified just over two years. He was sent to Heidelberg and Vienna to learn the technique of celloidin-impregnation as paraffin embedding did not seem to be a suitable technique for sectioning mosquitoes. On his return he set about sectioning and staining the mosquitoes Bancroft had sent and was soon able to show the various stages of the development of the embryos in the mosquitoes' tissues. One of his sections, more by luck than design, actually passed right through the whole length of a proboscis in which he saw embryos, in pairs, lying full length. This evidence strongly suggested that the embryos were injected into man at the time of the mosquito's bite but Low cautiously remarked, " without actual and somewhat dangerous experiment it would be rash positively to assert that the filaria is inoculated directly into man by mosquito bite ".[188] The necessary experimental proof could not readily be obtained with respect to the human filaria but in 1900 the ingenious experiment of Grassi and Noe all but demonstrated the transmission of the embryos of *Filaria immitis* of the dog by Anopheline mosquitoes. Grassi and Noe allowed a large number of Anopheles to feed on a filaria infected dog. Then, 15 days later, they liberated a number of these filarious mosquitoes in a small room with a healthy dog. Next morning they caught the blood-gorged mosquitoes and on dissecting them could find no embryos. Yet a batch of 15 mosquitoes which had not been fed on the healthy dog showed the presence of embryos in the proboscis. The inference was clear; all these mosquitoes were equally filarious yet those which had fed on the healthy dog had lost them in the act of biting.[189]

Chapter VIII

DRACUNCULUS MEDINENSIS

"IF any man will abandon his preconceived notions, and take the trouble to read Kuchenmeister's historical narrative of the *Dracunculus,* he will, I apprehend, find it very difficult to resist the conclusion that Moses was the first writer on this subject; and further, he will be well nigh necessitated to believe the 'fiery serpents' which afflicted the children of Israel during their stay in the neighbourhood of the Red Sea were neither more nor less than specimens of our *Dracunculus medinensis*". Thus wrote Cobbold in 1864.[190] The relevant passage in the Book of Numbers is confined to a single verse: "And the Lord sent fiery serpents among the people and they bit the people; and much people of Israel died".[191] Kuchenmeister, who was a considerable scholar, in particular with a good knowledge of Hebrew, devotes nearly four pages to a learned etymological discussion of this verse and arrives at the conclusion that Moses was describing an outbreak of dracontiasis. Meagre though the clinical account of Moses is, we have no reason to doubt the nature of the affliction. The Israelites were, at the time, in the region of the Gulf of Akaba, an area where the *Dracunculus* is endemic. We can be sure from our general knowledge of natural history that they were not plagued by true serpents and "fiery serpents" is no bad description of a worm which can be seen moving about beneath the skin, which gives rise to severe inflammatory reactions in the infected part and which is not infrequently fatal. The Greek geographer, Agatharchidas of Cnidus who lived in the second quarter of the second century B.C. and was tutor to one of the sons of Ptolemy VII gave a perfectly clear description of the condition stating "that the people taken ill on the Red Sea suffered many strange and unheard of attacks, amongst other worms (from) little snakes, which came out upon them, gnawed away their legs and arms, and when touched retracted, coiled themselves up in the muscles, and there gave rise to the most unsupportable pains ".[192] The Egyptian Papyrus Ebers, describes the treatment of a condition which was in all probability dracontiasis, and amongst the Greek and Roman writers Pliny, Galen, Paulus Aegineta, Soranus, Aetius and Actuarus all describe the condition.[193] Paulus Aegineta wrote, " In India and the upper parts of Egypt a class of worms called *Dracunculi,* resembling the intestinal, are formed in the muscular parts of the body, such as the arms, thighs, legs and in the sides of children, under the skin ".[194] Galen, who had never seen the condition, surmised that the worm was in fact of nervous origin; an opinion also held by Soranus. Among the Arabian physicians whose works deal with *Dracunculus* are Rhazes, Haly Abbas, Avicenna, Albucasis and Avenzoar. They, however, added nothing to the knowledge of this subject and generally considered that the parasite was either of nervous origin or else a degenerate vein and the condition was known as the Vena Medinae, for they appreciated its frequency in Medina.[195]

The European writers of the Middle Ages, who can have had little or no experience of the condition, added nothing to the subject and it was not until Europeans began to explore the tropics that any precise knowledge of dracontiasis began to be accumulated. Even then accounts of the disease by early travellers were received with incredulity. It must however be admitted that the following seventeenth century personal account of the disease is remarkably factual; "A few days after my arrival at Fort St. George in the East Indies the fruits of my Gengroon Journey shew'd themselves; for a little below the instep of my left foot, a worm put out its head, which afterwards cost me much trouble. These worms are bred by the Water, between Gengroon and Schiraz, especially that about Laur, they came out in any part of the body, and are very troublesome and dangerous, for I have known those who have kept their bed for them, some 6, some 10 Months, and some there are, who have lost sometimes their legs, sometimes their Lives by them; they come out sometimes to the length of 6 or 7 Yards; when they first come out, they are small like a thread, and upon a little bit of Stick or Cotton, and put upon them Onions and Flower of Rice boiled in Milk. The chief care is to be taken not to break them for then it is that they do Mischief. When mine first came out, for about

40 or 50 Days it came out every day by little and little, without putting me to much Pain but that I could go up, and down till it was come out a yard and a Quarter; but afterwards, one Day stirring too much, I hurt the Worm and inrag'd him, so that he broke off himself, and going in caus'd my Foot and Leg (up to the calf) to Swell till the Skin was ready to burst which kept me sleepless, and cast me into Fever. I had a Chirurgeon and kept my Bed for about 20 Days, in which I had several fits of the said Fever; the Worm was broke to pieces, and came out in several Parts of my Foot; but the Chirurgeon apply'd such things as kill'd the Worm, and turn'd it to Matter; he then Lanc'd my Leg a little above the Ankle, and another place of my Foot, and so with Drawing Plaisters drew it all out ".[196] In 1674 G. H. Velschius published his *Excercitatio de Vena Medinensi* . . ., in which, as Cobbold remarks, " we are amused, if not edified, by the numerous plates representing the old Persian surgeons extracting the Dracunculus ". Serious students of parasitology, being, during the eighteenth and nineteenth centuries, entirely domiciled in Europe had no experience of the condition and their writings were therefore able to contribute little but a more or less detailed history of the disease drawn from the ancient writers, hearsay reports and travellers' tales.

Amongst the first scientifically trained persons to give attention to the problems of dracontiasis were British Army medical officers serving in India about the beginning of the nineteenth century and their views on the subject are of interest. For example, James McGrigor, the well-qualified surgeon to the 88th Regiment, gave an interesting account of the disease in a memoir on the state of health of his regiment, between June 1st, 1800 and May 31st, 1801. Initially he remarked that " having never seen or heard much of this disease . . . I was not a little perplexed ". He found that the disease seemed to be endemic in certain small localities, for example, the Fort of Bombay. The 86th Regiment had been quite free of *Dracunculus* infestation on coming into the Fort in September 1799 but during the monsoon of 1800, 200 cases developed in the single unit. The 88th Regiment relieved the 86th in October 1800 but a few weeks later was embarked for Ceylon and during the voyage six cases developed. These seemed to be localized to a particular part of the ship and a detachment of artillery who ate the same food and drank the same water but who slept apart from the rest of the men on the gun deck were quite free of the disease.[197] Another surgeon, Ninean Bruce, surgeon to the 1st Battalion of the 88th Regiment, who himself suffered from the disease on the voyage, thought that he acquired the disease in the course of changing the dressings of infected men. He mentioned the possibility of acquiring it through drinking water but rather discounted this idea and thought it more likely that the ova of the worm were injected into the skin of the body by insects.[198]

Some years later Williams Scott, surgeon to the 1st Battalion Madras Artillery again noted the localized nature of the endemic areas. Thus the disease never occurred in troops permanently stationed at St. Thomas's Mount but was common in detachments encamped by the River Toomboodra. Scott examined a worm carefully under a microscope. The fact that he had a microscope suggests that he was an unusually enthusiastic medical officer and indeed something of a pioneer for at that time (1821), the microscope was hardly used in medical studies and was certainly not considered a necessary part of an army medical officer's equipment. He dissected a specimen with the aid of some tent needles and noted the milky contents of the body cavity but made no mention of the larvae. This perhaps indicates that his microscope was only of very low power, little more than a mounted hand lens, these being commonly referred to as microscopes. One particularly interesting observation which Scott made was that the worm tended to emerge when the affected limb was immersed in water. In this he was not original; the belief that this was so was general amongst the soldiers, and when one of his patients mentioned it he was sceptical, suspecting that, " Lilly's hint had some reference to a little liberty and a stroll to the river ". However, he allowed Lilly to sit with his leg in a bucket of water and found that the worm did indeed emerge. He then took him to a stream at the bottom of his garden and after three daily immersions the remains of the worm came away quite easily. Scott however did not grasp the significance of his observation. He suggested that the ova of the worm were deposited in the skin whilst the limbs were immersed in water.[199]

In Great Britain the disease was, of course, rare but George Busk, who was surgeon to the Seaman's Hospital, Greenwich claimed to have had many opportunities of observing the condition. He admitted, however, that a complete study of the parasite was not possible in this country and many gaps in our knowledge of it would have to be filled by workers in Africa and Asia. He was of the opinion that infection was acquired through exposing the skin to water and that this accounted for the frequency of infection in the legs. He supported this view by observing that in countries where the natives carried water in skins on their backs infection was often localized to this site. Busk's own researches were on the anatomy of the parasite and he stressed the necessity of microscopy in any parasitological investigation.[200]

Writing in the 1850's Kuchenmeister noted that "The mode of production of the worm in the human body is still enveloped in obscurity" and admitted that he had no personal experience of the parasite.[201] Cobbold, in his *Entozoa* published in 1864, summarized knowledge of the guinea-worm as it stood. It was known that the actual parasite was an adult female which was probably only parasitic during the final stages of its life and that it reproduced viviparously, liberating active embryos whose natural habitat was probably fresh water. The sexually mature male worm was unknown but was thought to be free-living in water. The sexes were supposed to associate in water during the monsoon season and then the fertilized female made its way by direct penetration of the skin into its host where it matured, producing the symptoms of dracontiasis only after about 12 months, when ready to liberate its embryos.[202]

The next steps in our understanding of this parasite was the discovery of its intermediate host which immediately necessitated an almost complete revision of the views on the life-cycle current at the time. This remarkable discovery was made by a Russian traveller Fedschenko. He was however indebted to R. Leuckart for the suggestion which set him on the right track. Leuckart had investigated a nematode parasite of certain fresh water fish such as the perch. He had discovered that the embryos of this parasite, *Cucullanus,* were swallowed by the minute crustacean, *Cyclops* from the gut of which it passed to the body cavity and underwent further development. Leuckart noted the close resemblance of the embryos of *Cucullanus* and *Dracunculus* and made the brilliant prediction that they had a similar life history. He therefore instructed Fedschenko to look for the further development of the embryos in some fresh water crustacean. Fedschenko had the opportunity to take up this problem on a visit to Turkestan in 1869. He obtained some larvae of the *Dracunculus* and put them in water with various insect larvae and crustaceans including some of the genus *Cyclops*. He saw the larvae penetrate into the bodies of the cyclops between the segments on the ventral surface whence they settled down in the body cavity and limbs, as many as a dozen being found in a single cyclops. After about 12 hours he found that the larvae shed their skins and began to grow and became fully developed in about five weeks. Fedschenko tried to rear adult dracunculi in dogs and cats by feeding them infected cyclops without success. Nonetheless it seemed certain that man acquired his infection in this way and that the simple precaution of filtering drinking water would effectively prevent dracontiasis. Fedschenko published his results in a Russian journal in 1869 and in 1873 visited Cobbold in London and reported his findings to him. A short while after this, again on his travels, he lost his life in a snowstorm in the Alps.[203]

Fedschenko's observations do not seem to have been immediately confirmed by other workers nor further attempts made to complete our knowledge of the life-cycle. In 1894 Patrick Manson confirmed Fedschenko's discovery of the development of the larvae using cyclops taken from a pond on Wandsworth Common and larvae from a patient with guinea-worm infestation under his care at the Albert Dock Hospital.[204]

Thus although the main practical problems concerning the life history of the *Dracunculus* had been solved there still remained a number of gaps which were but slowly filled in. The male guinea-worm had eluded detection, nor was the site of copulation known. Proof that man acquired infection by swallowing infected cyclops had not been obtained although the circumstantial evidence was very strong. R. H. Charles, working in Lahore, was probably the first to observe the male guinea-worm. He found at a post-mortem examination two female guinea-worms to which was clinging a much smaller worm about 4 cm. long.[205] In the early years of the twentieth century Leiper, working on the Gold Coast, discovered the male guinea-worms and showed experimentally that although the cyclops was killed by the concentration of hydrochloric acid in gastric juice, the contained larvae were not. By feeding a monkey bananas in which he had concealed infected cyclops, he proved that the guinea-worm was indeed transmitted in this way, for six months later five adult guinea-worms were found in its connective tissue.[206] Manson produced evidence that the guinea-worm took about a year to mature in the human tissues. He had, as patients, two friends who developed clinical signs of guinea-worm infection within four days of each other and whose only possible occasion of infection was a shooting trip in Uganda about a year before.[207] The actual site of copulation and the fate of the male parasite remains a mystery to this day.

Chapter IX

THE PARASITIC PROTOZOA

Introduction

THE development of the science of protozoology, of course, awaited the introduction of reasonably effective microscopes in the seventeenth century. Probably the first protozoon to be described was a calcareous foraminiferan, by Gesner in 1565, and Hooke, a century later gave a figure of a similar organism in his *Micrographia.* The birth of protozoology as a science can be dated exactly to the summer of 1674 when Leeuwenhoek observed some free-living ciliates in fresh water. Parasitic protozoology began a few months later when the same worker observed objects in the bile of a rabbit which were certainly the cysts of *Eimeria stediae*. He described them in a letter to the Royal Society in the same year as merely " oval corpuscles ".

In 1680 Leeuwenhoek observed a motile animalcule in the gut of a horse-fly and in 1681, in his own faeces, " animalcules a-moving very prettyly; some of 'em a bit bigger, others a bit less, than a blood globule . . . ". These parasites were in all probability *Giardia* which was therefore the first parasitic protozoon to be observed in man.

In 1683 Leeuwenhoek, whilst examining the blood of a frog which he was dissecting, noticed " a great number of living animalcules ". However, the blood was contaminated with fluid from other parts of the frog and on examining cleanly taken blood he found no more of them. A few weeks later, examining material from a frog's gut he " beheld an unconceivably great company of living animalcules, and these of diverse sorts and sizes ". These he went on to describe and they were almost certainly *Opalina* and *Nyctotherus.*[208]

For more than 100 years after Leeuwenhoek's observations there was virtually no progress in the study of parasitic protozoa although increasing numbers of free-living forms were described. The term

" protozoa " was introduced about 1820 and in 1838 Ehrenberg published his large work on the infusoria in which he described 350 species. Dujardin published an important treatise on the protozoa in general in 1841 and in 1845 in his *Histoire naturelle des helminthes . . ."* gives an up-to-date account of such parasitic protozoa as he accepts.

At this time the best studied group of parasitic protozoa were the gregarines, parasites of various insects. Dufour was the first to make a serious study of these parasites and gave them their name in 1828. Von Siebold in 1838 showed that the gregarines were widespread among various groups of insects and recognized that they were without a gastro-intestinal tract or a genital system. Dujardin noted the existence of the trypanosome which had recently been described by Gruby, and *Opalina* recently named by Purkinje. The other intestinal protozoa were grouped under the name " Chaos intestinale ", a term introduced by Bloch. One other group of parasitic protozoa was recognized and indeed relatively well studied, the sporosperms. These parasites, the first of that important group, the *Sporozoa,* to be described, were discovered by Müller in various species of fish in 1841. Dujardin recognized the similarity of these sporosperms with the bodies (*Monocystis*) often found in the testis of the earthworm.[209]

In 1836 Donné discovered the *Trichomonas vaginalis* of which he gave a full and accurate description in the following year.[210] The common and important parasite of rabbits, *Coccidium oviform* was recognized in the middle of the nineteenth century. The lesions produced in that animal were first adequately studied in 1839 by Hake but he regarded them as carcinomatous. Their true nature was gradually elucidated by a number of workers. Remak first established the intracellular nature of the parasite, the first such to be observed. Eimer made important studies of the development of the parasite in the epithelial cells of the mouse intestine. In 1858 a supposed case of human coccidiosis with post-mortem report was published.

Around the middle of the nineteenth century a number of human intestinal flagellates were discovered, none of particular importance. In 1856 Malmsten of Stockholm reported a case of severe diarrhoea in a man caused by rectal ulcers in which were found numerous ciliates looking like *Paramoecium* which were probably *Balantidium coli.* The first human protozoan parasite of major importance to be described was the amoeba of dysentery by Losch in 1875, but as late as 1886, no parasitic protozoon was generally accepted as the cause of any important human disease. As with the metazoan parasites the development of parasitic protozoology will be illustrated by examples drawn from certain important groups.[211]

Chapter X

THE TRYPANOSOMES

IN 1841 Professor Gabriel Valentin of Berne, whilst examining under the microscope the blood of a trout, noticed a dark, motile, bullet-shaped object lying between the blood cells. This, the first observation of a trypanosome, he briefly described in Müller's Archives for that year.[212] G. Valentin was born in Breslau in 1810 and after qualification settled in practice in his native town. In his spare time he worked at the microscope and in 1835 published an important work on comparative embryology. In the same year he also published, in collaboration with Purkinje, a classical paper on ciliary epithelial motion. In 1836 he was appointed professor of physiology in Berne, a position he held until 1881 when ill-health forced him to resign. He died in 1883. He was an excellent teacher and wrote useful textbooks of physiology, one of which was translated into English in 1853. He was also one of the earliest to appreciate the potential value of the spectroscope in physiological and medical research, publishing a monograph on the subject in 1863.[213]

In 1842 two other workers observed similar organisms in the blood of frogs and in 1843, David Gruby, in a short paper before the Academy of Science in Paris gave the first adequate description of the parasite. He named it *Trypanosoma sanguinis* because the motion of the organism resembled that of an auger or corkscrew (Greek: trupanon—a borer). Gruby was a distinguished microscopist just at the time when this instrument was beginning to be used seriously and effectively in biology and medicine. He was born of Jewish parents in South Hungary in 1810 and brought up in poverty. He managed, however, to graduate in medicine in Vienna in 1839, his graduating thesis being on the microscopical examination of pathological tissues. Settling in Paris, he did most important work in medical microscopy. He discovered *Microsporon audouini* and *Trichophyton tonsurans,* two of the causative fungi of human ringworm. He collaborated with Delafond, the veterinarian, in an important study of the Ophyroscolecidian parasites in the gut of horses, discovered a filaria parasite in the blood of a dog and was a pioneer photomicrographer. All his original work was done before 1845 when he gave up research and concentrated on practice. Despite his highly eccentric behaviour and prescriptions he was very successful, attending a number of notables such as George Sand, Chopin, Liszt and Dumas. He lived the life of a recluse. He died in 1898.[214]

In his paper on the trypanosome Gruby noted the recent discovery of parasites in the blood stream but pointed out that they were all *Filaria.* He had therefore systematically searched the blood of animals for parasites belonging to any other group such as were well-known in the intestine. He gave a good description of the trypanosome noting the undulating membrane which he likened to the blade of a saw. The trypanosomes were relatively uncommon occurring in only three out of 100 frogs. He felt that there was no doubt that the blood stream was the natural habitat of the trypanosome and that it had not strayed from some tissue, because its shape was so well adapted to that situation. He was interested in any possible relationship the parasite might have with disease but, since the frogs examined appeared healthy and he could not find any pathological lesion, concluded that the situation represented a physiological state.[215]

During the next two years trypanosomes were described in the blood of the fieldmouse and vole but it was really the observations of T. Lewis in 1878 which attracted attention to them as parasites of mammals. In July 1877 whilst investigating relapsing fever in Bombay Lewis noted numerous, highly motile organisms in the blood of about 29 per cent. of rats of two species, known to him as *Mus decumanus* and *Mus refesceus.* His description of them is less complete than that of Gruby, of whose work he was unaware, and his paper is illustrated with rather crude woodcuts. He pointed out that the rats harbouring this parasite, even in very large numbers, were quite healthy and suggested that this was evidence against the view that anthrax was actually caused by the bacilli present in the blood.[216]

Trypanosomes up till this time were mere curiosities of no particular importance. But, in 1880, Griffith Evans, a veterinary officer serving in the Punjab, discovered in the blood of horses, mules and camels affected with a fatal, febrile disease known as surra, a flagellate parasite similar to those seen by Lewis in the blood of rats. He concluded that the parasite was the cause of the disease and succeeded in transmitting it to a healthy dog and a horse. The presence of a flagellate organism in the blood in surra was soon confirmed by a number of observers, particularly by Steel, another veterinary officer serving in Burma. Steel, unlike Evans, thought that the organism was a spirochaete and proposed the name *Spirochaeta evansi*. Evans sent some slides of surra blood to a young bacteriologist, Edgar Crookshank, at King's College Hospital, London. Crookshank made a careful study of the organisms noting the presence of the undulating membrane. Clearly the organism was not a spirochaete but he failed to recognize it as a trypanosome, being apparently unfamiliar with Gruby's 42-year-old description.[217]

Evans did not know how the trypanosome of surra was conveyed from animal to animal although there was a native tradition that certain blood sucking flies (tabanids) were responsible for the spread of the disease. Evans mentioned this in his report and considered it possible. Other workers preferred the hypothesis of contaminated food or water. That a blood-sucking arthropod might convey the infection from animal to animal remained no more than a suspicion until after Bruce's demonstration of the aetiological role of the trypanosome and its transmission by tsetse-flies in nagana. Then observers in different parts of the world incriminated species of tabanid flies in the transmission of surra. But, unlike transmission of nagana by tsetse-flies, this was found to be a purely mechanical process, the trypanosomes not undergoing any development within the fly. The first person to demonstrate the mechanism by which surra was transmitted was Leonard Rogers in 1899, two years after the publication of Bruce's work on nagana. Rogers showed that the trypanosome of surra was transmitted by the bite of tabanid flies and that the flies remained infective for less than 24 hours. Bruce himself would not accept this and for some years refused to believe that trypanosomes could be transmitted by other than tsetse-flies, although that fly did not occur in India.[218]

Perhaps the most important contribution ever made to our knowledge of trypanosomiasis, was the investigation by David Bruce of the cattle disease of South Africa, nagana. However, before considering this investigation it is worthwhile drawing attention to a paper published by A. Laveran in 1892 because it gives a useful summary of all that was known about trypanosomiasis to that date. Although at that time trypanosomes were not known to be of any great medical or veterinary importance, Laveran was interested in trypanosomiasis as another example, the only other example known, of disease which was, like malaria, caused by a protozoon. He therefore thought it worthwhile to devote a few pages to a review of the subject. Laveran noted that trypanosomes had not been described in the blood of man but were known in the blood of birds, fishes, frogs, and some mammals. Their morphology was fairly well known and their method of reproduction in the blood had been well studied by Danilewsky in birds. However, he pointed out, many problems remained to be elucidated. It was uncertain whether the various trypanosomes represented a single species or several; their mode of transmission from one host to another was unknown, but it seemed likely that spread was via the gastrointestinal tract. Trypanosomes were attractive creatures for the protozoologist to study, being reasonably large, surviving well in blood or serum outside the body and being readily inoculable into other animals. This 11-page article with its 18 references summarized all that was known about trypanosomes in 1892.[219] Twelve years later such was the growth of the subject that the same writer was to publish a book of some 400 pages on trypanosomiasis. It is our present task to trace the more important steps in this expansion of the subject.

In 1894 Surgeon-Major David Bruce of the British Army contrived, with the aid of Sir W. Heley-Hutchison, the Governor of Natal, to have himself sent to South Africa to investigate a disease of cattle and horses known locally as " nagana ". Nagana is a Zulu word meaning " in low or depressed spirits " and refers to the salient clinical feature of the disease in animals. Bruce was at this time 39 years of age and, although his whole career had been spent in the army, was already a scientist of distinction. He had in 1886 discovered the cause of Malta fever and, in 1889, had been elected F.R.S. Since that time he had been assistant professor of pathology at the Army Medical College at Netley. Bruce and his wife, a doctor's daughter, who accompanied him everywhere at his own expense, acting as his laboratory assistant, arrived in South Africa in October. Towards the end of the month they left Pietermaritzburg and after a journey of 28 days by mule and ox-wagon arrived in Ubombo in Northern Zululand where they set up their primitive laboratory in a native hut.

Soon cattle suffering from nagana were brought to Bruce. The animals had fever, infiltration of the subcutaneous tissues with lymph, anaemia, were extremely emaciated and almost invariably died. Bruce, being a bacteriologist in the golden age of bacteriology, naturally suspected that the disease might be caused by bacteria and set about a bacteriological investigation. To his surprise he drew a blank and it is indeed remarkable that he was in a very short time able to eliminate bacteria as a cause without even following any false scents. This alone says a great deal for his technique under primitive conditions. The study of stained blood films was becoming popular owing largely to the work of Ehrlich and, his bacteriological studies having proved negative, Bruce determined to try this approach. He can have had little experience of this method for he used a not very suitable dye, carbol-fuchsin, as a stain. Finding occasional objects between the red cells which he was inclined to regard as staining artefacts he examined drops of fresh blood and found in his nagana cases an organism which he thought might be a filaria. Bruce had not, at that time, ever heard of trypanosomes. He found that if he injected blood from cattle with nagana into dogs he could produce a more acute disease with abundant trypanosomes in the blood. Bruce was thus able to define nagana by its clinical features, morbid anatomical appearance and by the "constant occurrence in the blood of an infusorial parasite".[220]

Bruce was aware that in Africa there was a common disease of domestic animals of the greatest economic importance. This disease had exerted a most profound influence on the whole history of the country and had been much described by travellers, hunters and missionaries—notably by David Livingstone. This condition was known as " fly-disease ". Since it is now known that " fly-disease " is none other than nagana we must briefly digress and trace the history of our knowledge of this condition. It seems that the first Europeans to encounter the " fly-disease " were the Portuguese in the sixteenth and seventeenth centuries who sent large expeditions inland along the lower Zambesi in search of gold mines. These expeditions ended in disaster as the horses succumbed to the bite of a fly. Left without their mounts the Portuguese soon fell prey to fever and hostile natives. As was later pointed out by Sir H. H. Johnston, " But for the Tsetse-fly the whole history of South Central Africa would be different "—it could have been traversed by mounted men and large quantities of goods could have been transported by wagons and pack animals instead of on men's heads. The fatal effects of the bite of a fly on cattle was noted in South Africa by Captain Harris, primarily a sportsman, in 1839. In 1850 Gordon Cumming, another hunter, referred to " the famous fly called 'tsetse' whose bite is certain death to oxen and horses ". The fly itself was identified by a French writer, M. Arnaud, in 1852 as a species of *Glossina*. From this time on many of the famous explorers of Central and Southern Africa gave more or less detailed accounts of the tsetse-fly. There are many references to the tsetse-fly in the *Journals of Livingstone* which had a very wide circulation and in 1865 his companion, Dr. John Kirk, published in the journal of the Linnean Society an admirable résumé of all that was known of the biology of the tsetse-fly. Kirk made many interesting observations on the biology of the tsetse-fly and took particular note of native opinions. He noted the regular accompaniment of big game with the tsetse-flies, the biting habits of the fly, etc. The natives were aware that in some places the " fly-belt " was so narrow that it was possible to drive cattle safely through provided it could be done at night. The natives also clearly distinguished " fly-disease " which was not contagious from the various other cattle plagues which were.[221] However, " fly-disease " and " nagana " were not known to be the same disease—Bruce himself had no suspicion of this when he noted his infusorial parasite in the blood of cattle with nagana. However, he had heard of " fly-disease " and was interested to see cases. It happened that " fly-disease " was prevalent on the lower slopes of Ubombo but not at the top where he resided.

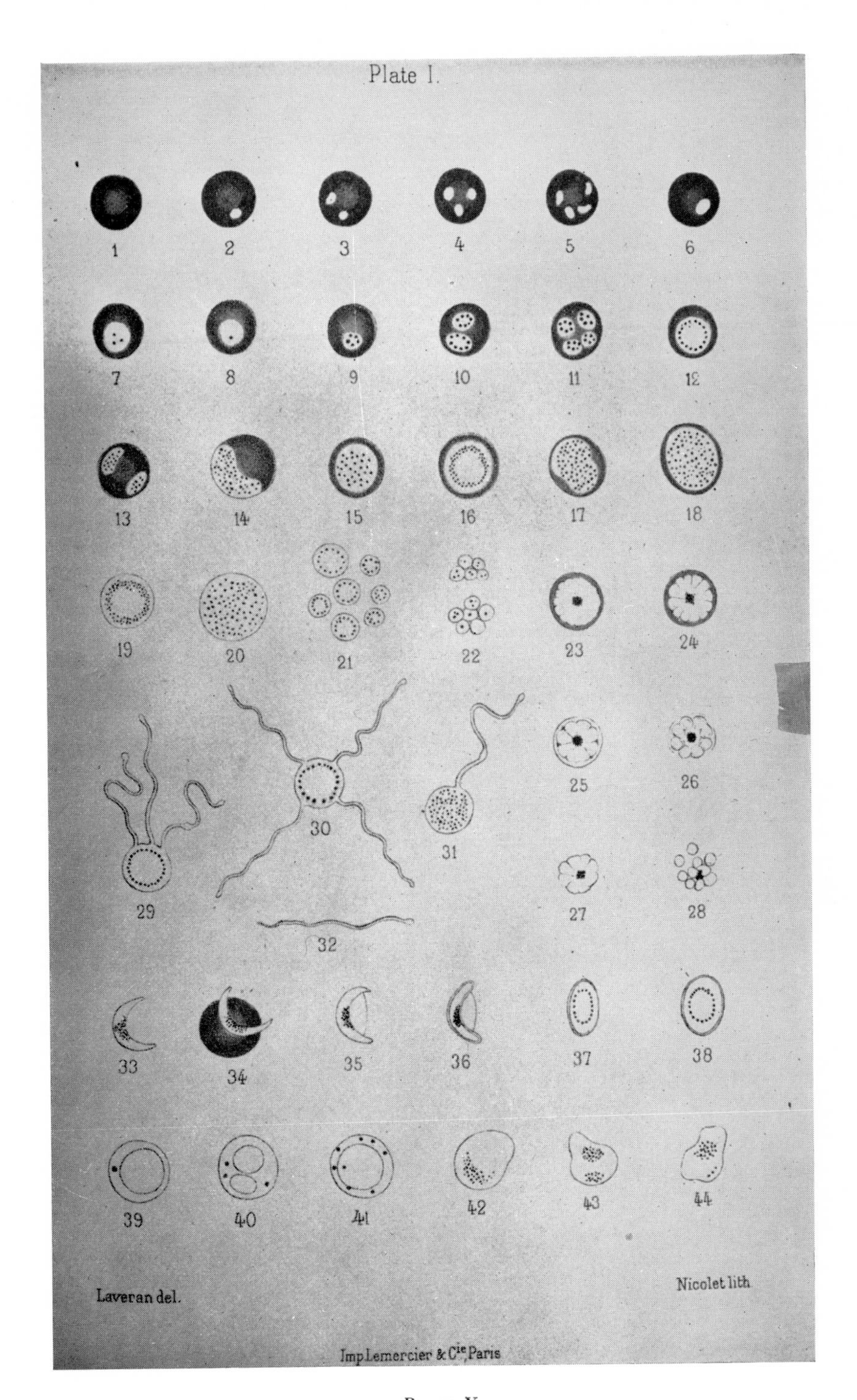

PLATE X

Laveran's drawings of malaria parasites—from his book *Paludism* (New Sydenham Society translation 1893).

[*To face p. 120*

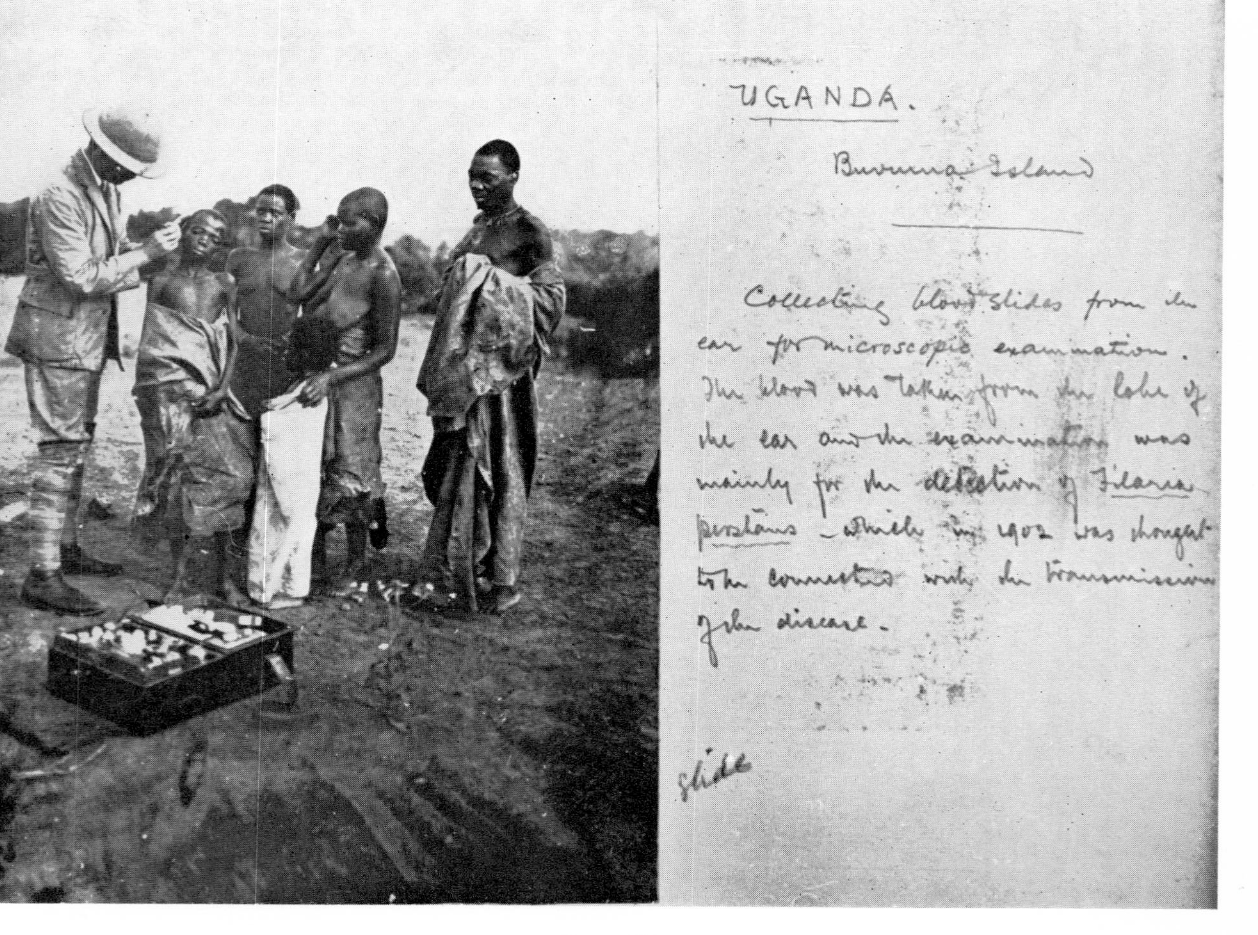

PLATE XI

Taking blood slides in the field. The first sleeping-sickness commission in Uganda 1902 (from an album of original photographs in the Makerere Medical Library).

PLATE XII

Dr. Christy at work in the laboratory of the first sleeping-sickness commission at Entebbe, 1902 (from an album of original photographs in the Makerere Medical Library).

To face p. 121]

PLATE XIII

A typical case of sleeping-sickness in Uganda 1902 (from an album of original photographs in the Makerere Medical Library).

He therefore sent two young oxen and some dogs into the " fly-belt " for a few hours. He was surprised to find, when they subsequently fell ill, that the same parasite was present in their blood as in the nagana cases.

Bruce was recalled to military duties on January 26th, 1895, the army authorities evidently feeling that they had not been sufficiently consulted with regard to his posting, and it was some months before Sir W. Heley-Hutchison was able to obtain leave for him to continue his investigations. However, on August 25th Bruce and his wife again left Pietermaritzburg for Ubombo where they arrived on September 8th. Now aware that " fly-disease " and " nagana " were one and the same condition, Bruce made a thorough study of the clinical and pathological features of the disease as it occurred in a variety of animals and also of the natural history of the tsetse-fly. But his main achievement during this period was to prove conclusively the role of the tsetse-fly in the epidemiology of nagana. Bruce set himself to answer the following questions: Is the tsetse-fly *per se* capable of giving rise to any disease in susceptible animals? Can the tsetse-fly convey nagana from sick to healthy animals and does it do so under natural conditions? How long does a tsetse-fly remain infective? Is the tsetse-fly capable of giving rise to nagana in a healthy locality? How long does the blood of a diseased animal retain its infective properties under various conditions?

Bruce has tsetse-flies brought up from the fly-belt to Ubombo and kept in captivity for some days " in order to give time for the haematozoon to disappear ". These were then allowed to feed daily on dogs for periods from ten days to two months. All the dogs remained quite healthy and thus Bruce concluded that the bite of the tsetse-fly *per se* was innocuous. He then took eight flies which had immediately before fed on a dog with nagana and allowed them to feed on a healthy dog. The procedure was repeated on several days and six days after the last batch of infected flies had fed, the dog was found, by microscopical examination of its blood, to be infected. Bruce concluded " from these two series of experiments it is seen in the first place that the fly *per se* does not give rise to any local or general disease . . . and secondly it proves that the fly can act readily as a carrier of fly-disease from affected to healthy animals ".

Bruce was puzzled by the fact that only the tsetse of all biting flies seemed to transmit nagana for he noted that other species of biting flies occurred in Ubombo but no cases of nagana. He was inclined to attribute this to some " anatomical peculiarity " of the tsetse-fly. It seemed important to determine how long a tsetse-fly might remain infective and he was able to show that even a fly fed 48 hours previously on an infected animal was capable of transmitting infection.

After some experiments with the blood of infected animals in which he showed that the parasite could under certain circumstances, particularly if kept moist, survive for four days outside a host, Bruce deemed it necessary to test his conclusions and discover whether or not " in a state of nature it (the tsetse-fly) really does convey the disease ". He therefore had healthy horses taken down for a few hours to the fly-belt but not allowed to feed or take water there. These then returned to the top of the hill and all subsequently developed nagana. Bruce recognized that although this strongly suggested that nagana was naturally acquired from the bite of the tsetse-fly, it did not provide absolute proof. He decided to bring the tsetse-flies to the horses. In the early morning flies were caught in the fly-belt and some four hours later brought up the hill and allowed to feed on healthy animals—they too developed nagana. Bruce therefore felt entitled to " consider it proved that the tsetse-fly does commonly, in a state of nature, convey the disease from animal to animal . . . ".

But if the tsetse-fly conveyed the disease to domestic animals the problem remained, where did the tsetse-fly acquire the specific parasite? An obvious answer was the wild game. This hypothesis fitted well with a strongly held local opinion " that where there is no game there is no Nagana ". At first Bruce thought that microscopical examination of the blood of wild game should settle the point but prolonged examinations of blood films from a variety of animals having proved negative he thought that possibly the parasites might be very few in number and that to inject fairly large volumes of blood into susceptible dogs would be a more sensitive test. Having first of all determined that blood retained its infective power when mixed with potassium citrate for seven hours he set out to shoot and bleed a variety of game from the lowlands below Ubombo. This blood he injected into dogs kept in the healthy area at the top of the hill. The experiments were highly successful for blood from buffalo, wildebeeste, bushbuck and hyaena were all found to be infective. Bruce wrote "These experiments I think prove that several species of wild animals inhabiting the Fly Country harbour the Nagana parasite, and the links in the chain of causation of this disease connecting the game through the Tsetse-fly with domestic animals are complete ".[222]

This was true enough but not the whole story for Bruce was both mistaken and very lucky. He believed that the tsetse-fly only remained infective for a relatively short time after biting an infected animal whereas, in fact, the fly does not become fully infective for a considerable period of time, 15 to 35 days. The trypanosomes undergo a cycle of development within the fly, eventually infective forms migrating to the salivary glands. What Bruce had observed in his experiments was only direct transmission, the tsetse-fly acting in a purely mechanical way such as a number of other blood-sucking flies are also capable of doing. It was not until 1906 that Robert Koch, working in German East Africa, suggested the trypanosomes went through cyclical changes in the tsetse-fly. He noted that sometimes in the fluid from the proboscis of wild tsetse-flies there were numerous trypanosomes but no blood cells which would suggest a recent feed and also that trypanosomes were present in the stomach of some flies, again in the absence of blood. However, Koch went on to describe a purely imaginary sexual cycle analogous to that of the malaria parasite.[223]

At the beginning of this century there was no record of trypanosomes infecting man. But in May 1901, a 42-year-old Englishman, master of a government launch on the river Gambia, was admitted to hospital at Bathurst with fever. The colonial service surgeon, Dr. Forde, naturally examined his blood for malaria parasites, apparently using a drop of fresh unstained blood rather than the more satisfactory stained films. He found no malaria parasites but was rewarded with the sight of many motile, worm-like bodies which he could not identify. The patient was sent home to England and admitted to the Royal Southern Hospital, Liverpool, where no malaria or other parasites were found in his blood. The patient improved without specific treatment and in December returned to Bathurst. He was, however, far from well on arrival and although not admitted to hospital was on the sick list. It happened that J. E. Dutton of the Liverpool School of Tropical Medicine was in Bathurst studying the local mosquitoes. He was asked by Dr. Forde to see the patient and, like Forde, found parasites in the blood which he recognized as trypanosomes. Dutton sent blood films to Laveran who reported that they were morphologically distinct from other known species and Dutton proposed to name the species *T. gambiense*. The patient meanwhile recovered his strength and early in January was fit enough to resume his duties.[224] A few months later a second case of human infection with a trypanosome was reported by Manson in a 40-year-old married woman from the Congo who also had a mild febrile disorder. Manson recognized the case because of its similarity to Dutton's patient.[225]

Dutton had meanwhile returned to Liverpool but in September 1902 he came back to the Gambia particularly to investigate human trypanosomiasis. Dutton had graduated in medicine at Liverpool in 1897 and was almost immediately attracted to tropical medicine. His promising career was however but short. After expeditions to Nigeria to work on malaria control and his investigations in the Gambia he set out with two companions, in 1903, to investigate relapsing fever in the Congo. Both he and his fellow worker, Todd, caught relapsing fever but recovered. However, in 1905, in a remote village two months' journey from the nearest telegraph station, Dutton died. In his short career he earned the respect of many distinguished scientists, including Robert Koch, and Sir Ronald Ross wrote of him that he had " never met any scientific worker for whom it was possible to have more respect and affection ".[226]

Dutton found that a very small proportion of the local natives harboured the parasite, apparently without any ill-effects, and suggested that the natives acted as a reservoir of infection which was occasionally transmitted to a European causing a mild febrile illness.

About this time an interesting thought occurred to Dr. Maxwell-Adams, another doctor working in the Gambia, that trypanosomiasis might possibly be but a stage in a much more serious and well-known disease—sleeping-sickness. He based his idea purely on certain common clinical features such as puffiness of the face, irritability, apathy and huskiness of the voice. Maxwell-Adams raised this possibility in print in the *British Medical Journal* in March 1903 and it is but just to pay tribute to this accurate piece of clinical observation for, unbeknown to him, his supposition had already been proved correct.[227] In 1901 the Cook brothers, missionary doctors in Kampala, Uganda, reported cases of sleeping-sickness and it was soon apparent that there was an extensive epidemic of the disease in Uganda. The Royal Society decided to sponsor a commission to investigate the disease in Uganda.

The commission consisted of three members: George Low, a 30-year-old Edinburgh graduate, who had come to London to assist Manson with his filaria researches. Low's part in tracing the cycle of the filaria in the mosquito and his participation in the famous malaria experiment in the Campagna have already been told. In 1902 he had just returned from a tour of the West Indies where he had been studying the distribution of filaria. Cuthbert Christy, the second member, had graduated in medicine at Edinburgh in 1892 and had travelled extensively in Africa, India, Central and South America. He was a fine field naturalist but quarrelsome and conceited. He actually came to blows with Low at Mombasa because their compartment in the train was labelled "Dr. Low and party". Christy has been described by one who knew him in Uganda as "a strange and ill-tempered man" and of seeming "more interested in butterflies than in tsetse-flies".[228] He spent his life in expeditions to Africa and was eventually killed by a rhinoceros in the Belgian Congo. The third member of the commission was Aldo Castellani, a 23-year-old graduate of the University of Florence. How he came to be chosen for this position and various interesting but not always accurate domestic details relating to this commission he has recounted in his autobiography. In April 1902 Castellani was a student at the London School of Tropical Medicine when, after one of his lectures, Manson asked for a volunteer to go with Low and Christy as bacteriologist. Inundated with applicants Manson held a competitive examination which Castellani won.[229] The composition of the various sleeping-sickness commissions which were to work in Uganda during the first decade of this century reflected the rivalries of personalities and institutions—Sir Patrick Manson and Sir Ray Lankester, the London School of Tropical Medicine and the Royal Army Medical Corps. The various commissions were rarely co-operative and jealousy between individuals was rife. A long and most interesting account of the " politics " of sleeping-sickness investigations in Uganda has been published which, as it is not directly concerned with the history of parasitology, will be omitted here.[230]

The commission left London on May 1st, 1902, travelled overland to Marseilles and thence by a comfortable P. & O. ship to Aden. The journey from Aden to Mombasa was made in an ancient and uncomfortable steamer. From Mombasa they went by train to the end of the line at Kisumu via Nairobi, then but a village with painted and befeathered warriors on the station to greet them. At Kisumu the party split up, Christy going to investigate an epidemic of unknown nature, whilst Low and Castellani made, by steamer, the three day voyage across Lake Victoria to Entebbe. They landed on July 11th and were met by Dr. R. V. Moffat, the principal Medical Officer.

The commission was allotted a two-roomed mud hut which was infested with termites but pleasantly situated on a small hill overlooking the lake from which a fine view could be obtained of hundreds of crocodiles enjoying their siesta on the warm sands. The commissioners had to set about constructing a laboratory and hospital for the study of sleeping-sickness. They rigged up a hut divided into two wards, for men and women, with another hut attached for a laboratory. This was divided by matting into two compartments, one for microscopical work and for the kerosene-operated incubator and the other for the preparation of culture media.

The commissioners started out knowing nothing about sleeping-sickness. There was one hypothesis as to its cause, which had been put forward by Manson, that the disease was due to infection with a species of filaria—*Dipetolonema perstans.* This idea Christy undertook to test by the laborious but sound method of mapping the geographical distribution of sleeping-sickness and *D. perstans* infestation. Christy appears to have been an indefatigable hiker and for almost his entire sojourn in Uganda was perpetually on the march. Having made his way from Kisumu on foot and by canoe to Entebbe where he arrived on July 26th, he again set out on August 6th to march along the north shore of the lake, inland to Lake Kioga, to the slopes of Mount Elgon and thence southward round the Gulf of Kavirondo along the eastern lake shore. He then returned along the lake shore by canoe and steamer to Entebbe by October 15th. As he went he plotted sleeping-sickness areas on a map and every 10-15 miles took blood samples from groups of the local population. On October 30th he set out yet again, this time south round the western lake shore down to German East Africa and back through the foothills of the Ruwenzori to Fort Portal and thence to Entebbe where he arrived on January 31st. Here he found that Low had already gone home, and instructions awaited him ordering him to do the same. This he did by marching north to Gondokora, on the Nile in the Sudan, and thence by boat down to Cairo. In his wanderings Christy collected some useful epidemiological information. He noted that sleeping-sickness was found only close to the shore of Lake Victoria and was never found more than 15 miles inland. *D. perstans* infestation, however, was much more widespread and therefore unlikely to be connected with the disease. The distribution of persons with enlarged cervical lymph nodes did however correspond with the distribution of sleeping-sickness. He collected mosquitoes but found no correlation between any particular species and the distribution of the disease. All his epidemiological information pointed to an association with low-lying shambas along the shore and inlets of Lake Victoria. He noted that no cases had occurred amongst Europeans although many missionaries lived in close association with the natives and suggested that perhaps their clothing protected them.[231]

During Christy's absence Castellani had been studying cases of sleeping-sickness both clinically and at post-mortem, including bacteriological investigations. He had managed to cultivate a streptococcus from the heart blood in a high proportion of cases and was inclined to think that he had discovered the cause of the disease. However, on November 12th, 1902, he noticed a few trypanosomes in the centrifuged deposit of some cerebrospinal fluid from a case of sleeping-sickness. There is some doubt as to whether Castellani immediately appreciated the significance of this finding. On the one hand he certainly did not abandon his streptococcus but on the other, when a second commission consisting of David Bruce and D. N. Nabarro arrived on March 16th, he refused to tell Bruce of his discovery of the trypanosome unless the latter agreed that the discovery should be published under Castellani's name alone and that Bruce's colleague, Nabarro, should not be told at all.

It is hardly to Castellani's credit that he laid down such conditions nor to Bruce's that he accepted them. However, Nabarro having been put to work on the clinical side, Bruce and Castellani working from morning until night, had by the time the latter left on April 6th, examined cerebrospinal fluid from 34 cases of the disease finding trypanosomes in 20. In 12 control cases they found no trypanosomes. As soon as he arrived in England, Castellani published an account of these observations, that the trypanosomes were the cause of sleeping-sickness, but that also his streptococcus played a part in the pathogenesis of the disease.[232] He took upon himself the whole credit for the discovery but Bruce, having honoured his part of the bargain initially, nonetheless wrote in a later report, " For the sake of the future historian " that "At the time of the arrival of the commission he (Dr. Castellani) did not consider that this trypanosome had any causal relationship to the disease, but thought it was an accidental concomitant like *Filaria perstans* . . . As Dr. Castellani has not entered into any detail respecting these matters in his reports, it is thought advisable to supplement his account with the above, as the history of the discovery of the cause of any important disease must always be of interest ". Such was the ethos of the sleeping-sickness investigators in 1902.

Bruce returned to England at the end of August but before then the basic facts of the aetiology and epidemiology of sleeping-sickness were established. Bruce and Nabarro soon confirmed that trypanosomes were almost always to be found in the cerebrospinal fluid of the sleeping-sickness patients but not in the healthy population and with his experience of nagana Bruce naturally suspected the possible role of the tsetse-fly in transmission. He therefore proposed to compare the geographical distribution of tsetse-fly and sleeping-sickness. An explanatory letter and instructions for the collection of biting flies was drawn up and dispatched to missionaries and officials all over Uganda. The

Sir David Bruce (1855-1931). (From *Obituary Notices of Fellows of the Royal Society*. London 1932.)

Lady Mary Elizabeth Bruce (1849-1931). Wife of Sir David Bruce. (From *Illustrated London News*, Dec. 3, 1931.)

Aldo Castellani (1878-). (From Olpp, G. (1932), *Hervorragende Tröpenarzte in Wort und Bild.*, München: Otto Gmelin.)

Carlos Chagas (1879-1934). (From Olpp, G. (1932), *Hervorragende Tröpenarzte in Wort und Bild.*, München: Otto Gmelin.)

PLATE XIV

[*To face p. 128*

Camillo Golgi (1843-1914). (From Anton Mansch, *Medical World, c.* 1906. Berlin-Charlottenburg: Eckstein.)

Sir Patrick Manson (1844-1922). (From an original photograph in the Wellcome Collection.)

Sir Ronald Ross (1857-1932). (From *The Illustrated London News,* 1932.)

PLATE XV

To face p. 129]

response was excellent. In June, July and August 460 collections of biting flies were received and sorted into tsetse and non-tsetse-flies. If a parcel contained tsetse-flies a red mark was made at that location on a map, if not, a blue mark. The similarity in distribution of tsetse-fly and sleeping-sickness was immediately apparent.

The commission also made a detailed study of the distribution of tsetse-fly on the Entebbe peninsula and found that the flies were confined to the lake shore where there was forest. They were not found on the open sandy beaches, on grasslands or banana plantations. They showed also that monkeys were susceptible to sleeping-sickness and that tsetse-fly fed on human cases would transmit the disease to monkeys, as also would some captured wild tsetse-flies. They concluded " that sleeping-sickness is, in short, a human tse-tse fly disease " and that the causative trypanosomes were transmitted by the bite of *Glossina Palpalis* " and by it alone ".[233]

During the next four years the activities of the sleeping-sickness commission were kept up by the succession of R.A.M.C. medical officers, Captain Grieg, Lieutenant Gray and Lieutenant Tulloch. A certain amount of detail was filled, animal trypanosomiasis studied, but no discovery of fundamental importance was made. They reported, in 1903, the first case of sleeping-sickness in a non-African, a Persian who lived near the lake shore at Entebbe. There was however soon to be another case. In the early part of 1906 Lieutenant Tulloch suffered several bouts of unexplained fever and on March 12th trypanosomes were found in his blood. He and Gray left Uganda on April 3rd travelling down the Nile. There was no treatment for sleeping-sickness and the disease was invariably fatal. Tulloch, knowing he was doomed, bore his illness with cheerfulness and courage and died on June 20th, 1906, aged 27 years.[234]

With the departure of Gray and Tulloch the original series of commissioners came to an end but a colonial service medical officer, A. D. P. Hodges, was left in general charge of the sleeping-sickness problem. He set about energetic clearing operations on the Entebbe peninsula and effectively wiped out sleeping-sickness from that area. In 1906 a serious attempt was made to control the disease in Uganda, based on Bruce's observations that the tsetse-flies and the disease were confined to the lake shore. It was argued that if native population was evacuated from the area the infected flies would die out and after an interval the healthy population could return. This policy was put into effect in 1906 by Sir Hesketh Bell. When this policy had been in operation for about two years Bruce returned to Uganda, for it was important to be sure that the tsetse-flies around the lake shore were no longer infective before the native population was re-admitted. Wild tsetse-flies were therefore caught and fed on monkeys but some of them developed sleeping-sickness. How was this failure of Bruce's policy to be explained? There seemed to be three possibilities: that infected tsetse-flies could live for more than two years, that the reservoir of infection was maintained by illicit native inhabitation near the lake or that some animal acted as a reservoir for trypanosomes. An attempt was made to test this last idea by inoculating blood of various wild birds and mammals into monkeys but always with negative results.[235]

It seemed that much more would have to be discovered about the natural history of the tsetse-fly before effective control of the disease would be possible. A most important worker in this field was G. D. H. Carpenter. He was the son of an Eton schoolmaster, himself an entomologist of distinction and F.R.S. Educated at Oxford and St. George's Hospital he qualified in 1908, joined the Colonial Medical Service in 1910 and was sent to Uganda. During the next 10 years he made extensive studies of the habits of the tsetse-fly, often living for long periods alone on infected islands on Lake Victoria. Some of the problems he tackled were as follows:—

(1) The estimation of tsetse-fly density in different localities. His method was to send out trained native fly-catchers and after half-an-hour to whistle them in and count their catch. Density was expressed in fly-boy-hours.

(2) The measurement of the longevity of tsetse-flies by catching large numbers, marking them by amputating their legs, releasing them and recounting at intervals. In one experiment in which 8,000 flies were used Carpenter found flies which had lived as long as 182 days.

(3) The possibility that there might be natural animal predators on tsetse-flies. Carpenter examined the stomach contents of numerous birds, tree frogs, and lizards with negative results.

(4) The conditions most favourable for the development of the tsetse-fly larvae with the object of creating attractive artificial areas where the larvae could be destroyed.

(5) What was the taste of the tsetse-fly in food by examining the blood in the stomachs of wild flies. He was only able to distinguish between mammalian and non-mammalian blood microscopically. He found that 79 per cent. of flies contained non-mammalian blood and only 21 per cent. mammalian. In May 1911 Carpenter made an important observation. In the blood of two antelopes which he shot on Damba Island a trypanosome morphologically identical with *T. gambiense* was present. He also showed that wild flies from the island were infective for monkeys. The population of the island had been evacuated.[236] Carpenter eventually retired from the Uganda Medical Service in 1930 and in the year 1933 was appointed Hope Professor of Zoology at Oxford. He died in 1953.[267]

In 1912 Dr. H. L. Duke, in a survey of a number of islands on Lake Victoria, found that on islands where there were buck the tsetse-flies were infective for monkeys, whereas on islands where there were no buck the tsetse-flies appeared to be non-infective.

Meanwhile, in 1910, another observation of the greatest interest had been made. Dr. J. W. W. Stephens of the Liverpool School of Tropical Medicine discovered a new species of human trypanosome. Whilst examining the blood of a rat, said to be infected with *T. gambiense,* for teaching purpose, he noted that the trypanosomes had unusual morphological features—a proportion of the organisms had their nucleus situated posteriorly. The trypanosome had been taken from the blood of a patient with sleeping-sickness at that time under the care of Ronald Ross in the Royal Southern Hospital, Liverpool. Stephens took a further blood sample from the patient, injected it into a rat and again found the particular type of trypanosome. Further experiments showed that this form was more virulent for rats and guinea-pigs than the usual *T. gambiense.* Moreover the patient from whom the strain had been derived had never been to an area where *T. gambiense* or *Glossina palpalis* was known to occur. He had acquired the disease in N.E. Rhodesia in an area where *G. morsitans* was abundant. For all these reasons Stephens believed that he was dealing with a new species of trypanosome which he named *T. rhodesiense*.[239]

In January 1912 Bruce headed yet another sleeping-sickness commission, this time to Nyasaland, with the particular object of ascertaining the importance of wild game as a reservoir in human trypanosomiasis. He set up camp on Kasu Hill, about 30 miles from the shore of Lake Nyasa. The scrub between the hill and the lake abounded with game and tsetse-fly. Bruce's plan was to shoot animals, take a sample of blood, and transport it to the camp-laboratory as quickly as possible by motor cyclist, for microscopy and for injection into dogs, goats and monkeys. Out of 180 animals examined, from elephants down, nearly one-third were found to harbour trypanosomes, apparently *T. rhodesiense*. Bruce wished to compare these trypanosomes with those from cases of nagana—*T. brucei*. He therefore had such a strain sent to him from Zululand, from the very spot where he had himself discovered the organism. On examination this strain was found to have a morphology indistinguishable from *T. rhodesiense* and Bruce was therefore " driven to the conclusion that *T. rhodesiense* is neither more nor less than *T. brucei,* and that human trypanosome disease of Nyasaland is nagana. To this may be objected that nagana has never been known to attack human beings. This has probably been due to faulty diagnosis, cases in man being returned as malaria ". It was further concluded that, " It is self-evident that these wild animals should not be allowed to live in fly-country, where they constitute a standing danger to the native inhabitants and domestic animals. It would be as reasonable to allow mad dogs to live and be protected by law in our English towns and villages . . . ". The commission therefore recommended a policy of complete " blotting out " of wild animals in tsetse-fly areas, but in tsetse-fly areas only, for trypanosomes were not found in the blood of wild animals outside the fly-areas.[240]

The carrying out of such a policy would have been difficult and expensive and moreover was intrinsically repugnant. Also, opinion amongst the experts about the importance of the animal reservoir of human trypanosomes was by no means unanimous. The British Colonial Office appointed an inter-departmental committee to investigate the question of the necessity and practicability of a policy of game destruction which reported in May 1914. The committee were of the opinion that "hasty and imperfectly considered action of a drastic character, such as an attempt to effect a general destruction of wild animals is not justified by the evidence . . .". The committee stressed the importance of destroying the tsetse-fly and pointed out that the policy of moving peoples out of fly-infected areas appeared to have controlled the Uganda outbreak of sleeping-sickness. It was pointed out that the distribution of tsetse-flies and trypanosome-harbouring game was much more widespread than was human trypanosomiasis. Even Bruce and his colleagues, despite their rather sweeping recommendation, had doubts as to whether the animal trypanosome was pathogenic for man. All they could say was that the animal and human trypanosomes were morphologically identical, developed in the same way in the tsetse-fly and behaved in the same way in the experimental animal.

One day the Bruce commission was visited in its camp by a German worker, Taute. Taute said that he was convinced that the two trypanosomes were distinct and was willing to demonstrate it on himself. However, he declined to do the experiment in Bruce's camp as it was situated in an area where human trypanosomiasis certainly occurred. Taute said he would retire to the other side of the lake, where there was no human trypanosomiasis, and there conduct the experiment. Taute soon reported that he had failed to become infected by the bite of an infective tsetse-fly and by the inoculation of infected blood. The British commission were still not convinced, maintaining that it was Taute who was immune to trypanosomiasis. After the First World War Taute repeated his experiments in Portuguese East Africa, this time inoculating himself, his colleague Huber and 129 natives with the rhodesiense-like animal trypanosome, none becoming infected. Even this experiment by no means convinced everybody that the two trypanosomes were distinct, it being argued that man was normally very resistant to infection but that certain strains of enhanced virulence might be pathogenic for man.[241]

Epidemiological evidence was also against the idea of the identity of the human and animal trypanosome. The well-known fact that in nagana country man never became infected had been rather unconvincingly dismissed as due to faulty diagnosis. In 1927 W. D. Dye, a medical officer in the Tanganyika Medical Service, published a most interesting paper describing a careful study, by straightforward epidemiological methods, of a small outbreak of trypanosomiasis in his district. Dye drew up a map showing the degree of game-density and fly-density on which he marked the various villages, distinguishing those which were well cleared and so free of tsetse-fly from those which were infested. For each village the number of cases of sleeping-sickness and estimated population were given. Examination of the map showed that although there were many villages which were similarly situated with regard to the fly and game density of the area, cases of sleeping-sickness were virtually confined to those villages which were tsetse-fly infested. It seemed therefore that being bitten by flies in the villages was the source of infection. One of the villages in Dye's area, Namaboa, had only been founded just over 2½ years. It was badly cleared and fly-infested and yet for 2½ years was quite free of sleeping-sickness. However, when sleeping-sickness occurred soon 44 out of the population of 115 fell ill of the disease. This evidence strongly suggested the introduction from an outside source of an infected case with subsequent man to man transmission. Dye had all the survivors of Namaboa removed to a camp and detained for some months, the sick and healthy being separated. Healthy natives, free of trypanosomes were then allowed to return to the village. This was now even more overgrown and heavily infested with tsetse-flies yet no further cases developed. Dye pointed to one other fact of significance, the frequency of family outbreaks or groups of cases occurring in adjoining huts. In one village in which the huts were widely scattered in small groups of one to three all the cases occurred in one group of huts, evidence very suggestive of man to man transmission.[242]

Another observant medical officer in the Tanganyika Service stressed the importance of economic and social factors in the epidemiology of sleeping-sickness. He pointed out that, before the coming of Europeans, the natives lived in large, well cleared villages for security and sleeping-sickness was rare. With the establishment of law and order, the suppression of tribal war and slave-raiding many small " bush villages " had been established. These were not well cleared and the contact between man and tsetse-fly increased. In addition the suppression of slavery had led to a decline of large-scale agriculture and so had movements of population to fill the labour demands made by European enterprise.[243]

Economic factors played a dominant role in control measures in Uganda. There were two opposite tendencies: that of population "concentration" when people moved together into prosperous areas in times of boom and that of "reclamation" when people moved outwards in time of slump to areas which might be dangerous. Government policy could influence the course, either prohibiting habitation in dangerous areas or else helping in the proper clearing of areas. Administration wavered between these two policies, on the whole favouring the prohibitive measures because it was the most economical. But prohibitive measures could not always be enforced. Famine in 1918 caused a population migration along the lake shore and resulted in a sharp outbreak of sleeping-sickness. A 1919 further food shortage made fish an important article of diet and native poachers, some 1,500 of them, earned about five times the normal wage in this way. Furthermore, there was a public outcry when the Government proposed to put a stop to poaching. Sir R. Coryndon's administration saw that proper reclamation was the ideal policy, for tsetse-flies cannot exist in a densely populated and intensively cultivated area. As much as could be done in this way on a budget of £4,000 per annum was tried on the Sese Islands and was successful.[244]

South American Human Trypanosomiasis

In 1910 a new human infection with a trypanosome was reported in rather unusual circumstances. A 40-year-old Brazilian, Carlo Chagas, an assistant in the Oswald Cruz Institute was put in charge of the antimalarial measures during the construction of a new railway in the province of Minas Geraes, Brazil.

In the course of his journeying in these remote parts of Brazil he heard of a species of Reduviid bug which infested the houses of many of the inhabitants. This unpleasant creature, rather over one inch long, lived in cracks in walls and other places of concealment by day and indeed until all lights were extinguished. It then sallied forth and obtained a blood meal by biting the inhabitants, particularly on the face. This character had given it local names such as the "barber" or the "kissing-bug". Chagas dissected a number of these bugs and found numerous flagellates of the crithidian type in their hind-guts. He sent a number of the bugs back to the institute where Oswald Cruz, the director, allowed them to bite a marmoset monkey. A month later the monkey was found to have trypanosomes in its blood stream which appeared morphologically distinct from any known species. Chagas showed that guinea-pigs could also be infected and in this animal he thought that the trypanosomes went through a process of schizogony in the lungs and so named his new parasite *Schizotrypanum cruzi*. However, it was soon shown that the lung parasites were of quite a different species and Chagas reverted to the name *Trypanosoma cruzi*. He studied the life-cycle of the parasite within the Conorhinus and thought that after development in the gut the infective form of the parasite migrated to the proboscis ready for inoculation. Thus far Chagas was well acquainted with the parasite but it was not associated with any human disease although he found the characteristic trypanosomes in the blood of some of the inhabitants of the bug-infested houses. However, Chagas suspected that the trypanosome might be the cause of an acute febrile disease of children characterized by oedema, particularly of the eyelids, anaemia and glandular enlargement which sometimes proved fatal. Soon he was able to demonstrate the trypanosome in two such cases. Although the laboratory aspects of the work had outstripped the clinical and the record of the cases was meagre, it was thought that "Chagas has not left much for his successors".[245]

In 1916 Chagas published a paper in which he gave an account of 29 cases, 11 of which had proved fatal. He also thought that the parasite invaded the thyroid gland and was responsible for the common cretinism and goitre of Brazil as well as a variety of other syndromes. In 1917 Torres drew attention to the cardiac lesion of Chagas' disease and although gradually it became apparent that most of the syndromes Chagas claimed to be due to the trypanosome were not so caused, a definite chronic type of disease, in addition to the acute disease of children was delineated.

Meanwhile, however, there was not universal acceptance of Chagas' view that the trypanosome was inoculated into man by the bite of the bug. In 1912, Brumpt, in Paris, found that although the bite of the infected Conorhinus was not infective for mice, inoculation of the bug's faeces intraperitoneally was infective. He went on to show that faecal material could infect mice via the unbroken conjunctiva and rectal mucosa. Brumpt's view was that faecal material was probably transmitted from the skin of the victim to the conjunctiva or oral mucosa when bitten on the face. The habit of the bug to defaecate on feeding was well established. Chagas opposed this concept of the mode of infection for the rest of his life but the matter was finally settled by Dias, working in the Oswald Cruz Institute in the last years of Chagas' life. In the early 1930's Dias allowed 104 infected bugs to feed on 14 guinea-pigs, taking precaution against faecal contamination. No infections resulted. However, mucosal contamination always produced infection.[246]

CHAPTER XI

ENTAMOEBA HISTOLYTICA

DYSENTERY has always been a common, widespread disease and was well known to the ancients. Important as it has been as a disease of the population as a whole, it is as a disease of armies that it has been most devastating and to which it has been commonly more destructive than powder and shot. Not infrequently must this disease have affected the course of history by its sudden appearances in the camp of contending armies. In the Federal Armies, during the American Civil War there were over a quarter of a million cases and Volume II of the *Medical and Surgical History of the War of the Rebellion* was described by Osler as "the most exhaustive treatise extant on the intestinal fluxes".[247]

We must not however allow ourselves to digress too far into the history of acute dysentery, for the parasite whose story we are about to chronicle, *Entamoeba histolytica,* probably played but a minor part in the acute decimation of armies in the field. Nonetheless, military medical officers, particularly those stationed in the tropics, were familiar with both the dysentery now known to be due to the dysentery bacillus and that due to amoeba and it was their clinical acumen, sometimes combined with a zealous study of morbid anatomy, which first pointed a distinction between the two diseases, long before either parasite was known.

Amongst the earliest of these investigators was James Annesley, a medical officer in the military service of the East India Company for nearly 37 years. He assiduously noted the signs and symptoms of the various diseases he encountered and utilized every opportunity to conduct post-mortem examinations. In 1828 he published his classic *Researches into the Causes, Nature and Treatment of the More Prevalent Diseases of India . . .*" based on his personal experience. He was acquainted with a form of dysentery "of remarkably frequent occurrence in India " which he called " hepatic dysentery " in which the clinical picture and morbid anatomical features of dysentery were accompanied by structural disease of the liver. Of the importance of this connection he was well aware but doubtful as to the nature of the relationship. He was however inclined to attribute the dysentery to " a morbid state of biliary secretion " although well aware that often the dysenteric symptoms preceded signs of liver damage. Hepatic dysentery not infrequently terminated in abscess of the liver, and of both conditions and their combinations Annesley gave excellent accounts, particularly of their morbid anatomy, clearly based upon practical study. With regard to the cause of dysentery Annesley incriminated cold nights, intoxicating liquors, noxious terrestrial exhalations, fatigue, exposure to the night air, and even intestinal worms, although he considered the last of little importance considering their prevalence amongst those unaffected by dysentery.[248]

The parasite responsible for the chronic and hepatic types of dysentery was discovered in 1873 by Dr. F. Lösch, a clinical assistant to Professor Eichwald of St. Petersburg. Lösch discovered the amoeba in the stools of a young Russian peasant, named Markoff, who had contracted dysentery in St. Petersburg. This was not the first occasion on which amoebae had been found as parasites of man. Another Russian, G. Gros had, in 1849, discovered and briefly described an amoeba parasitic in the mouth. In 1860 Lambl of Prague reported the finding of amoebae in the intestine of a child dead of enteritis, although R. Leuckart doubted the accuracy of Lambl's descriptions and was later supported in this view by C. Dobell who managed to obtain the rare original papers of Lambl.[249] Certainly Timothy Lewis and D. D. Cunningham in 1870 in the course of their studies on the aetiology of cholera observed amoebae in human faeces. They regarded the amoebae as non-pathogenic and it is indeed likely that the specimens they saw were of the non-pathogenic species, *Entamoeba coli*.

Thus it is almost certain that Lösch was the first to observe the *Entamoeba* of dysentery and he left, moreover, a good account of the clinical features, post-mortem findings and parasitology of his patient in a long, detailed paper in *Virchow's Archiv*—a journal with a wide circulation, in 1875. In the bloody, mucous stools he found large numbers of very active amoebae some 20-30 μ in diameter with an ectoplasm clearly differentiated from the endoplasm, a vesicular nucleus and sometimes containing ingested red blood cells. He attempted to infect four dogs both per os and per rectum with the amoebae. One of the dogs did develop dysentery, and on dissection was found to have ulcers in the mucosa of the large intestine containing numerous amoebae. When his patient died, Lösch found a comparable condition in his large intestine. He did not, however, conclude that this parasite was the cause of the patient's dysentery, but rather believed that they acted as irritants which prevented the healing of the ulcers originally caused by some other agent.[250]

Although it might be supposed from the clear-cut observations of Lösch that the role of the amoebae as a cause of human dysentery would have been established quite rapidly, this was not the case. Indeed the researches of many workers all over the world during the next 40 years were necessary finally to define the role of this parasite in human pathology. The confusion that followed hard on Lösch's observations appears to have stemmed from the failure to appreciate that there were more than one species of amoeba parasitic in the human intestine, not all of which were pathogenic, and that dysentery was not a single pathological entity but had more than one causative agent. Thus there were patients without dysentery who harboured amoebae and patients with dysentery in whom prolonged search failed to reveal them.

The next important observation on the amoebae of dysentery was made by Koch in Egypt in 1883 in the course of his studies on the aetiology of cholera. During his investigations Koch had occasion to make post-mortem examinations of five cases of dysentery, two of which were complicated with liver abscesses. Sections of intestinal ulcers in four of these cases showed peculiar bodies of variable size and shape which Koch appears to have regarded as amoebae. They were also present in the wall of one of the liver abscesses. However, Koch was immersed in his cholera studies and did not follow up his observations. But his work stimulated a young Greek physician, by the name of Staphanos Kartulis, at that time working in Alexandria, to make an intensive study of the endemic dysentery of Egypt.

The studies of Kartulis were spread over the next 20 years and, although varying in accuracy, did much to establish the amoeba as a cause of tropical dysentery. He examined 150 cases of dysentery and claimed to have found amoebae in them all, and yet, in a control series of non-dysenteric patients, never found the parasites. Both claims are hardly credible; some of his dysentery patients must have been bacillary and any competent worker would have found carriers of amoebae amongst the healthy population in Egypt. He was, at first, unable to infect laboratory animals but eventually succeeded in transmitting the infection to cats. He also claimed to have cultured the amoebae on artificial media. No doubt he did cultivate some amoebae but it is unlikely that they were *Entamoeba histolytica.* Two other important observations he did make: in 1887 he reported the presence of amoebae in the pus of a liver abscess, thus demonstrating the common aetiology of dysentery and hepatitis, so long suspected, on clinical and pathological grounds. In 1904 he published an account of amoebae in a cerebral abscess.[251] Despite inaccuracies in detail, medicine is indebted to Kartulis for drawing attention to amoebae as pathogenic organisms. His papers were published, for the most part, in *Virchow's Archiv* and thus had a wide circulation. It was his work that drew William Osler's attention to the subject. Writing to a friend, in March 1890, Osler commented "We have been much excited over Kartulis' amoebae which we have found in a liver abscess from a case of dysentery".[252] Osler reported this case in the *Johns Hopkins Hospital Bulletin*—the first to be diagnosed in America. He appreciated the possible importance of the parasite, remarking "It is impossible to speak as yet with any certainty as to the relation of these organisms to disease. The subject is deserving of extended study, and a point of special interest will be the determination of their presence in the endemic dysentery of this country".[253] A few months later, his house-physician, H. A. Lafleur, reported a further case at a meeting of the Johns Hopkins Hospital Medical Society. Lafleur and William Councilman of the same hospital's pathological department showed the parasite to be common in Baltimore and published in 1890 the most exhaustive account of the disease in English. Their work is a classical contribution to the pathology of the disease although adding nothing to our knowledge of the amoebae concerned. They were responsible for the introduction of the terms " amoebic dysentery " and " amoebic abscess of the liver ". They also introduced the important concept that there might be two species of amoebae infecting man, one pathogenic and the other non-pathogenic, but did not bring forward evidence in support of this idea.[254]

However, in 1893 H. Quinke, professor of medicine at Keil, with his colleague E. Roos was able to provide evidence in support of the contention of Councilman and Lafleur. Quinke and Roos had but one case of dysentery to study but they studied it most carefully and controlled their observations by a study of amoebae from non-dysenteric cases. They noted all the essential characters of *Entamoeba histolytica,* its size, clear ectoplasm, active movement and ingested red cells and confirmed its pathogenicity for cats. By contrast they showed that the amoebae from non-dysenteric cases were larger, sluggish in movement and never contained red cells. They were also the first to observe the encysted form of the parasite and demonstrated that these were infective by mouth for the cat. They correctly concluded that this was the mode of infection in man.[255]

This fundamentally important work failed to attract the attention it merited and, as Dobell remarked, " by one of those curious blunders which so often arrest the progress of science, their observations were almost ignored by their contemporaries " and although, by the mid-1890's, all the main facts necessary for understanding the part played by amoebae in human pathology were known, it required another 20 years of painful work and many a retrograde step before the truth became generally accepted. It was the opinion of Dobell, who combined a scholarly knowledge of his subject with extensive practical experience, that Fritz Schaudinn was chiefly responsible for this period of confusion.[256] This indefatigable worker accomplished much for protozoology in a working life of but 12 years. Born in 1871, he studied zoology at the University of Berlin, graduating with a thesis on a new genus of Foraminifera in 1894. After a visit to Bergen to collect material, he settled as assistant in the Berlin Zoological Institute and worked particularly on the reproduction of rhizopods. He stressed the importance of determining the details of the whole life-cycle in protozoa. His first parasitological work was on the coccidian Eimeria, whose life-cycle he worked out and in which he demonstrated a type of sexual reproduction. He also confirmed the work of Ross and Grassi on the life-cycle of malaria parasites and pointed out their similarity with coccidia. In 1901 the Kaiserliche Gesundheitsamt, appreciating the importance of protozoa as human pathogens, decided to set up a division of protozoology and sent Schaudinn to Rovigno to study pathogenic protozoa prior to taking charge of the new department. It was here that he did his work on parasitic amoebae. Schaudinn took up his appointment at the Kaiserliche Gesundheitsamt in 1904 and in the two short years left to him worked on ancylostomiasis, and halteridia, and discovered the spirochaete of syphilis, for which he is today chiefly remembered.[257] In 1903 Schaudinn published the results of his observations on the intestinal amoebae in which he described an entirely imaginary form of asexual reproduction by process of "budding off" of small daughter amoebae and an equally unfounded type of sexual reproduction. He failed to observe the highly important cysts described by Quinke and Roos. He did however agree that there were two species of human intestinal amoebae, one pathogenic and the other non-pathogenic. Whereas Quinke and Roos had been ignored, so great was Schaudinn's authority that this important point was thenceforth widely but not universally accepted. Schaudinn also bestowed upon the intestinal amoebae the names by which they are known. He called the pathogenic species *Entamoeba histolytica* although it would have been more correct to have retained the specific name "coli" given by its first observer Lösch. The non-pathogenic species he named *Entamoeba coli.*[258]

In the same year that Schaudinn published his findings, Dr Huber presented, at a meeting of the Society for Internal Medicine in Berlin, the case of a former "China Krieger" who had developed dysentery in that country. This was a typical case of amoebic dysentery and in addition to describing the vegetative stage, which he definitely regarded as pathogenic, he described the cysts which he believed to form part of the life-cycle of the amoeba and showed that they were infective to cats by mouth. He distinguished them from the cysts of *Entamoeba coli* but although he told Schaudinn of these observations they were ignored.[259] The issues were further clouded by the work of W. E. Musgrave and M. J. Clegg working in the Philippines. They were unable to distinguish one species of amoeba from another and came to the conclusion that " all amoebae are or may become pathogenic ".[260]

Thus at the beginning of the twentieth century the part played by amoebae in human dysentery and hepatitis was far from settled. At a meeting of the tropical section of the British Medical Association a discussion on dysentery was opened by Andrew Duncan. He stated flatly that he " would advance the view that the amoeba has nothing to do with dysentery in that country (India) as a causative agent " and, furthermore, " that the large tropical abscesses (of the liver) do not bear any special relation to antecedent dysentery, but that multiple abscesses do ".[261] Duncan's views were opposed, however, in the next paper which was read on behalf of a 34-year-old I.M.S. officer, Leonard Rogers, who had just spent a few months as acting pathologist in Calcutta—" that paradise of tropical pathologists ".[262] Rogers had examined a considerable number of patients with dysentery and with liver abscesses, always finding the amoebae. He showed that the pus of a newly opened liver abscess was invariably sterile and that even if amoebae could not be found in the pus, they could always be found in scrapings taken from the wall of the abscess cavity. An analysis of the clinical and autopsy records of the Calcutta Medical College showed that in 95 per cent. of cases of liver abscess there had been antecedent dysentery of the amoebic type. During the first 12 years of his service as pathologist in Calcutta Rogers maintained his interest in amoebiasis making contributions of importance to knowledge of its pathology, diagnosis and treatment. In 1903 he published a paper describing the pathology of the disease in the liver showing how the amoebae spread from the gut to the liver via the portal veins. He accounted for the absence of dysentery in some cases of liver abscess by showing that sometimes the intestinal lesions were confined to the upper part of the large bowel. He showed that diagnosis of liver abscess could be assisted by counting the leucocytes in the peripheral blood. A considerable leucocytosis of the polymorphonuclear type was usual. However, although polymorphonuclear leucocytes might account for up to 80 per cent. of the increased white cells they never accounted for 90 per cent. These findings were important in two respects: the fever which accompanied the development of amoebic hepatitis was commonly diagnosed as malaria. Both Sir William Osler and Sir Patrick Manson agreed that they rarely saw a case of liver abscess which had not already been treated with full doses of quinine. But in malaria there was never a leucocytosis. Hepatitis sometimes resulted in basal pleurisy and symptoms suggestive of lower lobe pneumonia. In pneumonia, as in hepatitis, a leucocytosis is usual but Rogers pointed out that in pneumonia the polymorphonuclear leucocytes usually accounted for over 90 per cent. of the increase.[263]

Throughout the first decade of the century confirmatory evidence of the causal role of amoebae in human dysentery gradually accumulated. On the far side of the world from Rogers, Captain C. F. Craig of the United States Army, first in San Francisco and later at Fort Leavenworth, Kansas, reported a study of 1,579 cases of amoebic dysentery, demonstrating the truth of the distinction of a pathogenic and non-pathogenic species on morphological grounds.[264] But pathologists as a whole did not find it easy to identify the *Entamoeba histolytica.* Even so experienced a protozoologist as Wenyon, as late as 1913, regarded the clear distinction of the various species of human intestinal amoebae " as one of the most difficult problems facing the protozoologist who is interested in human pathology " and thought that it would hardly be done satisfactorily until some method of cultivating them *in vitro* was developed.[265]

Sir Patrick Manson was not absolutely convinced that the *Entamoeba histolytica* was the causal agent of tropical dysentery. He wrote in 1909, " Thus the occurrence of amoebae in the stools of healthy individuals and their absence from the stools of a proportion of cases possessing the clinical characters of the type called ' amoebic ', suggest caution in definitely accepting the micro-organisms as the true cause of this type of dysenteric disease, and the suspicion that after all it may be merely an epiphenomenon ".[266] Manson admitted the clinical

10

and pathological relationship between dysentery and liver abscess but again, remarkably in the face of the very considerable accumulation of evidence, did not feel able to come down firmly on the side of the amoeba as the causal agent. Moreover, he devoted a separate chapter in his textbook to "Tropical liver", a condition which, as Rogers was to point out, was probably non-existent and in fact was a dangerous myth leading to failure to diagnose and treat early cases of amoebic hepatitis. Manson painted a quaint picture of the aetiology of tropical liver. "The young European who finds himself in the tropics for the first time is surrounded very often by luxuries in the shape of food, wine, carriages, servants—luxuries to which he had not been accustomed perhaps in his home . . . Little wonder, therefore, that in such circumstances the youth having the appetite and the opportunity of gratifying it, is apt to indulge in food and drink beyond safe physiological limits. He is made lazy by the heat; he cannot exercise during the day, and when evening comes, he prefers lounging on the veranda or hanging about the club bar to walking or games . . .". All this led to an unusual amount of work for the liver, hyperaemia of the organ and "tropical liver".[267]

It was the work of E. L. Walker of the biological laboratory of the Bureau of Science in Manila between 1910 and 1913 which Dobell has described as "one of the most brilliant contributions ever made to medical zoology" that once and for all settled the essential outline of the subject. Walker showed that the amoebae which several workers such as Musgrave and Clegg had been able to cultivate artificially from human faeces were, in fact, derived from ingested cysts of saprophytic species belonging to the genus *Amoeba* and that the parasitic species of man were two clearly distinct species of the genus *Entamoeba,* one of which was pathogenic and the other which was not.[268] He was able to prove that man acquires his infection by swallowing the cystic forms. Out of 20 volunteers, Filipino prisoners in Bilibid jail, fed amoebae or cysts, 18 became infected, as judged by the appearance of cysts in the faeces, the incubation period varying from 1 to 44 days. But of these 18 volunteers only four developed clinical dysentery.

Walker also showed that the host determined whether or not overt dysentery ensued upon infection. He fed a man with cysts who duly became an excretor of cysts although symptomless. He further passaged the strain of amoeba through two more men producing the carrier state but not the clinical diseases. A fourth man however fed cysts from the third man's faeces came down with typical amoebic dysentery 20 days later.[269] Walker published his findings in two excellent papers in the *Philippine Journal of Science* in 1911 and 1913. The second paper described his extensive feeding experiments and occupies 75 pages—the whole issue of the journal. He pointed out that the epidemiology of amoebiasis was the same as that of typhoid fever and that the same prophylactic measures should be employed.

The stationing of numerous British troops in the Middle East during the First World War and the Gallipoli campaign renewed interest in, raised problems concerning, and provided opportunities for extensive studies of amoebiasis. Little of first-rate importance was discovered, but the difficulties of diagnosis were investigated and the epidemiological studies of Wenyon in Alexandria emphasized the importance of the carrier in the spread of the parasite. One point of interest discovered independently by Wenyon and C. Dobell was that there were several distinct "races" of *Entamoeba histolytica* distinguishable on the size of their cysts. Wenyon described two "races" with cyst diameters of 7-10 μ and 15-19 μ while Dobell claimed that there were at least five. The races did not appear to differ in pathogenicity or geographical distribution.[270] D. W. Cutler, an assistant lecturer in Zoology at Manchester University, doing war work for the Medical Research Committee in Professor Dean's department of pathology, succeeded in cultivating the *Entamoeba histolytica in vitro* on a medium based on a boiled extract of human blood-clot and showed that amoeba grown *in vitro* retained their pathogenicity for cats.[271]

One product of the wartime studies on amoebiasis which should not be overlooked was the publication in 1919 of Clifford Dobell's classical monograph *The Amoebae Living in Man*. Dobell had devoted a great part of his working life to the study of amoebae from the zoological point of view. The literature on the subject had grown rapidly but, as the preceding account may have indicated, considerable confusion existed. There was no modern, accurate account of the parasitic amoebae of man and this gap Dobell set himself to fill. The book describes, in some 140 pages, all that was known of the six species of amoeba known to infect man. Dobell compiled his bibliography with scholarly care claiming that "few works of material importance from the zoological standpoint have been omitted". He corrected errors of previous bibliographers and went to any trouble necessary to see rare works on his subject.

Chapter XII

BABESIA BIGEMINUM

NO history of parasitology would be complete without some account of the remarkable investigations of Theobald Smith into the aetiology and epidemiology of Texas fever. At least two entirely novel facts in relation to parasitology as a whole arose out of this investigation; that a protozoan parasite might be transmitted by the bite of an arthropod vector and that a parasite might be transmitted by the arthropod vector to its progeny. In addition many other interesting observations were made particularly on immunity to protozoan infections.

Theobald Smith was born in Albany N.Y. in 1859, the son of German immigrants to the U.S.A. His father was a tailor by trade. After doing well at school in Albany, Smith won a state scholarship to Cornell University where he studied biology and mathematics. In 1881 he entered Albany Medical School from which he graduated M.D. in 1883 having spent one spring semester during this time in the biology department of the Johns Hopkins University. Brilliant student that he was, he deserves no credit for so rapid a mastery of medicine, for this was in the unreformed days of American medical education when the normal medical course at Albany was but two years. Smith's interests already lay in the scientific aspects of his profession, particularly the rapidly growing science of bacteriology. Unable to afford to go abroad to sit at the feet of the great Continental masters, Smith stayed at home and taught himself bacteriological technique. His German background stood him in good stead for he was able to read that language perfectly.

After a short period of post-graduate work in biology at Cornell, Smith's first job was as pathologist to the Bureau of Animal Industry in Washington. Here he worked for 11 years before going to Harvard as Professor of Comparative Pathology. His first four years were spent doing a variety of bacteriological studies, particularly developing the technical side of the work. His chief at this time was D. E. Salmon, a veterinarian whose name is perpetuated in the bacterial genus *Salmonella*. Salmon was nine years Smith's senior, had trained at Cornell University and done a period of post-graduate study at the well-known Alfort Veterinary School in Paris. Salmon's department had been started in 1878 one of its principal objects being the study of the epizootic diseases of Southern cattle, particularly the so-called Texas fever.[272]

Texas fever, a severe and often fatal infection of cattle had been known since the end of the eighteenth century but it was not until about 1868 that it began to be a serious problem on account of widespread, devastating epizootics amongst Northern cattle which had been exposed to cattle from the Southern states, or even allowed to graze on pastures recently inhabited by Southern cattle. A number of investigations into the aetiology of the disease were made by various investigators and several germs falsely incriminated. The most useful of these early investigations was that by Salmon who carefully defined the line, the 37th parallel, north of which the disease was not endemic. The most valuable facts about the disease were the accumulated observations of farmers and stock-breeders who had noted that apparently healthy Southern cattle when driven north caused outbreaks of the disease in Northern cattle during the summer months only. They were harmless in winter. It had also been noted that actual contact between Northern and Southern cattle was not necessary, that Northern cattle grazed on land recently harbouring Southern cattle became infected and that cattle ticks were constantly associated with the disease. In 1889 Salmon set Smith to work on the problem of Texas fever giving him F. L. Kilborne as a veterinary associate. Smith studied Texas fever continuously for the next four years finally reporting his results in a classic monograph in 1893. Bulloch was of the opinion that this work could be " re-issued as a textbook to show how scientific work should be done ".[273] Smith and Kilborne's study embraced four main aspects of Texas fever; (1) its symptomatology, pathology and diagnosis, (2) the causative agent, (3) the mode of transmission of the disease and (4) immunity to the disease. These studies were carried on concurrently as opportunity offered but may here be dealt with separately.[274]

Clinical and Pathological Aspects

Smith and Kilborne found that the main clinical features of the disease were fever and severe haemoglobinuria. There were two types of disease, the first acute and usually fatal which occurred in the summer months and a milder, usually non-fatal type in the autumn. The essential pathological change appeared to be a severe haemolytic anaemia. They counted the red cells in the blood and found that counts might fall from over 6 million per cu. mm. to less than 2 million in two or three weeks. The morbid anatomy of the condition appeared to be secondary to this, the main features being an enlarged spleen, the cut surface of which was of a dark " blackberry jam " appearance, and microscopically showed intense congestion with red cells. The liver was the organ most seriously involved showing enlargement, congestion, bile-injection and fatty degeneration. The kidneys also were enlarged, congested and sometimes showed haemorrhages and epithelial degeneration. The other organs of the body were substantially normal. Their account of the pathology, gross and microscopic, is in itself a masterly contribution.

The Causative Agent

A consideration of the essential pathology of the disease, the destruction of the red cells, convinced Smith that it was in these cells that he should search for the cause of the disease and in the very first case which succumbed on the experimental station at Washington in 1889 he found certain micro-organisms in the blood. Some of the red cells were found " containing two pale bodies of a pyriform outline ". These bodies he went on to describe minutely, noting that on the warm stage of a microscope some of them exhibited sluggish movement. He stained them with alkaline methylene blue and other dyes and found that not all the parasites existed in the form of double pyriform bodies. There were smaller single, irregular bodies in some of the cells. The proportion of red cells infected in the peripheral blood was usually between 1 and 10 per cent. but in organs such as the liver, spleen and kidneys a far higher proportion was found to be infected. However, in the milder, autumnal type of the disease the parasite appeared in a different form, much smaller than the large pyriform bodies but a much higher proportion of the red cells were infected.

But, as Smith was careful to point out, the assumption that these bodies were living parasites and that they were the cause of Texas fever " without further proof would undoubtedly be open to objection . . . ". He therefore devoted considerable attention to a microscopic study of their structure and to differentiating them from various known red cell inclusion bodies. Although it seemed highly probable that these bodies were parasites he conceded that ideally one should cultivate them outside the body and reproduce the disease in animals " by methods akin to those of bacteriology ". However the close association of the presence of parasites with disease and with relapses made it virtually certain that they were the causative organisms. Added to this he showed that the artificial inoculations of blood from an infected animal into a healthy animal reproduced the disease which was accompanied by the presence of the intracellular organisms. With regard to the nature of the parasite, Smith considered it to be a protozoon but felt that it could not be fitted into any of the three known groups of intracellular parasites of red cells, *Haemogregarina, Haemoproteus,* or *Plasmodium*. He therefore proposed a new genus " *Pyrosoma* " giving the organism the specific name " bigeminum ".

The Transmission of Texas Fever

Smith took as his starting point the more or less prevalent theory of cattle owners, whose districts had occasionally been invaded by Texas fever from the South, that ticks were the cause of the disease. Unlike earlier workers he was not satisfied " of the absurdity of the idea ". However, apart from the suspicions of the cattle owners, there was no positive data in favour of the idea when he began work in the summer of 1889. The tick itself was not unknown to science for it had been described under the name *Ixodes bovis* by Professor C. V. Riley in 1868. Little was known of its life-history but when its possible importance in Texas fever was appreciated, Dr. Cooper Curtice, also of the

Bureau of Animal Industry, began a careful study of the creature. Curtice found by accident that adult female ticks confined in a glass bottle always lay their eggs and these eggs, which would hatch out in a dish of soil kept in a warm place, formed the starting material for his investigation. Curtice fed the larval ticks on cattle and followed them through their moults to adult ticks. He also gave them a new name " *Boophilus bovis* ".

Smith himself confirmed and extended the work of Curtice. He noted particularly the high ambient temperature that was necessary for the development of the eggs and that an unfed, young tick could survive for many weeks. Experiments to determine the role of ticks in Texas fever were begun in the summer of 1889 at an experimental station half a mile outside Washington. Seven head of cattle were imported from a permanently infected area in N. Carolina. They were rather thin and carried a large number of ticks in various stages of development. The experimental station consisted of a pasture some 50 yards square which could be divided into a number of smaller fields. In the first experiment four of the Southern cattle were placed in one small field on June 27th along with six Northern cattle. Of these Northern cattle three were dead of Texas fever before the end of August, two more were killed whilst ill and one developed the disease but recovered. The Southern cattle were removed from the field on August 17th and at intervals from August 20th onwards a number of Northern cattle were admitted to the field. Eight cattle were added and of these five died of the disease. So far nothing new had been learned but this preliminary experiment had been designed to furnish material with which to work and to act as a control for the second experiment. For this a different enclosure was chosen and into it were put the other three N. Carolina cattle, but only after all their ticks had been carefully picked off by hand. Perhaps it was this aspect of work which led Smith later in life to refer to his Texas fever investigations as " four years of slavery ". Then four Northern cattle were admitted to the enclosure with the tick-free Southern cattle. The experiment was begun on July 27th and by September 6th no disease had appeared amongst the Northern cattle so two of them were transferred to the first field where both of them became ill with Texas fever.

The results of these preliminary experiments seemed clearly to indicate the importance of ticks in transmission of the disease and steps were immediately taken to repeat them. In September nine more head of cattle were imported from N. Carolina. Exposure of Northern cattle to these animals did not result in the devastating disease of the first experiment. The animals passed through a mild form of the disease and recovered. Again Northern cattle were exposed to Southern cattle from which the ticks had been removed without any of them falling ill. One final experiment was done in 1889, the exposure of Northern cattle to ticks alone. On September 13th several thousand ticks were scattered over yet another enclosure and the following day four Northern cattle were admitted. Three of them contracted Texas fever. Thus in the first four months of his investigations Smith had traced the basic pathology of Texas fever, described the causative organism and proved that ticks played an essential part in its transmission. Looking back it seems surprising that he should devote yet another three seasons to the study of the disease, particularly as in later life he admitted that his "interest in a problem usually lagged when certain results could be clearly formulated or particularly applied". Yet all who knew him agree that Smith was a perfectionist, meticulously careful and thorough. Results which would have convinced the majority of workers, he had to confirm again and again.

In the summer of 1890 he repeated the previous year's experiments but also instituted others to determine whether or not the ticks had survived the winter in the field. They had not. He obtained four head of cattle actually from Texas to make sure that the disease transmitted by them was the same as that caused by the N. Carolina cattle. His most important experiment of 1890 was that which showed that the young ticks artificially hatched in the laboratory could transmit the disease. Hitherto he had believed that the tick carried the disease between the infected Southern cattle and the soil of the Northern pastures, the ticks when dead liberating a resistant spore which was taken in with the food. However, feeding an animal with grass from a very infected field failed to produce the disease and made this hypothesis untenable.

It had also been noticed that animals exposed in a field immediately after it had been infected with ticks did not die until some 50 to 60 days had elapsed whereas those exposed on the same land 30 days after infection died within 15 to 25 days. Furthermore all the animals which succumbed had young ticks on them—it seemed as though the disease was associated with the appearance of a new generation of ticks. He therefore had a yearling heifer placed in a box stall and a number of young ticks, hatched artificially in glass dishes, fed on the animal; it developed Texas fever with the characteristic parasite present in the blood. This experiment was repeated three times with exactly the same result. The implications of this experiment were so important that Smith could not wait for the following season to follow it up. He therefore had a stable kept warm at a temperature between 65° and 80° F. by means of a coal stove. He found that under these circumstances the disease could be produced at any time of the year provided that the temperature was high enough for the ticks to develop.

The season of 1891 was devoted entirely to confirmatory experiments and that of 1892 mainly to determining whether or not Texas fever could be transmitted without ticks. Animals were fed large numbers of ticks in various stages of development without result. One other experiment of interest was done this year. Smith tried to test for the presence of infection in the young ticks by grinding some up in water and injecting them into cattle. No disease resulted but, as Smith pointed out, this merely emphasized our incomplete knowledge of the life-history of the parasite.

Immunity to Texas Fever

The striking difference in immunity to disease caused by the Pyrosoma between Southern and Northern cattle formed the basis of the fatal outbreaks in the latter. In the course of his studies on the epidemiology of the disease Smith was able to make some important observations on the immunology of Texas fever. It was commonly said by cattle owners that Southern cattle kept on Northern pastures for some time lost their immunity. In July 1890 Smith therefore exposed six Southern cattle from the previous year to cattle fresh from N.

Carolina. Two of them developed a slight infection but the rest appeared immune. It was also of interest that two calves of Southern parentage, but born at the experimental station, developed only slight infections on exposure to the disease. Going over his carefully kept records, Smith found that during 1889, 1890 and 1891, 24 head of cattle over one year old had been exposed to infection. Of these only one animal remained unaffected. The remainder suffered severe or fatal disease. By contrast, of eight calves which had been exposed only two died although all became infected. It seemed clear that the young animals were relatively immune to the disease and that the immunity of the Southern cattle might depend upon their early exposure to the disease which caused them subsequently to be immune. Smith re-exposed the various Northern cattle which had recovered from attacks of Texas fever and found that they had acquired some degree of immunity. Of 18 re-exposed animals seven remained unaffected but of the other 11, three died. One attack of Texas fever therefore did not give complete immunity. Smith was however not hopeful about the possibility of preparing a vaccine to prevent the disease because an attack of the disease did not give immunity and there was no known way artificially to cultivate the parasite. However, now that the epidemiology of the disease was understood, proper preventive measures could easily eliminate the disease from Northern pastures. The problem of moving Northern cattle south was more difficult but Smith suggested two possibilities: taking only young animals with their partial natural immunity or exposing older cattle to infection during the autumn, when a mild disease was invariably contracted, in the hope that some degree of immunity might be acquired.

All who have studied this work of Theobald Smith on Texas fever have been struck by its simple elegance. De Kruif wrote, " never, I say, has there been written a more simple but at the same time more solid answer to an enigma of nature " and with this estimate Bulloch, the most distinguished and critical of historians of microbiology, agreed. The present writer might add that the reading of Smith and Kilborne's report *Investigations into the Nature, Causation and Prevention of Texas or Southern Cattle Fever* has been one of the most enjoyable experiences in the composition of this history.

The details of the development of Pyrosoma in the tick were not finally worked out for 40 years after Smith's work. In 1906 Robert Koch attempted to elucidate the cycle of the parasite in the tick and described a process of emigration from the red cells in the gut of the tick with subsequent fusion of gametic cells. It was not until 1931 that E. W. Dennis in California observed the fusion of identical looking gametes in the lumen of the tick's gut with the formation of a mobile zygote which passed through the gut wall and invaded the ovary.[275]

Texas fever was not in fact confined to the Southern parts of the U.S.A. nor was Theobald Smith the first to see the parasitic cause of the disease. A similar disease was known in Rumania and was there investigated by V. Babes, director of the Pathological and Bacteriological Institute in Bucharest. In 1888 he described an intra-cellular parasite in the red cells of affected cattle. However, he claimed also to be able to transmit the disease to rabbits and to have cultivated the organism on bacteriological media. His work was of no significance in the development of our understanding of the disease. Nonetheless the parasite of Texas fever now bears the name *Babesia bigeminum* in his honour.[276]

Chapter XIII

THE PLASMODIA

As Sir Philip Manson-Bahr has remarked of the history of malaria "There can be nothing so unpalatable as a tale retold which is a bare recital of dry and unadorned facts . . .". The story of the development of our knowledge of malaria has indeed been told on numerous occasions and, moreover, anything approaching a detailed account would exceed in length the entire remainder of this short history of parasitology. Yet we cannot ignore a parasite of such enormous importance and, besides, the story of our knowledge of the plasmodium of malaria is one of the most fascinating in the whole history of medicine.

The bibliography of this chapter will refer the reader to sources where a more detailed account of this topic may be found. But, though this chapter can be little but a bare recital of unadorned facts, there may be a place for a brief account of how the most important points in the biology of the parasite of malaria were discovered and of the lives of the discoverers. It happens that some of the characters involved in the solving of the malaria problem were of a jealous and acrimonious disposition and scarcely any topic of medical research has excited so much controversy over matters of priority and credit.

There are three main aspects of the history of our knowledge of malaria which any outline sketch must take into consideration. This is the story of the discovery of the parasite, the story of the development of the parasites in the human body and of the different species and their relation to the clinical manifestations of the disease. Finally there is the story of the development of the parasite outside the human body and its transmission by the mosquito. There is much more to a full history of this disease but these features constitute the heart of the matter parasitologically and are all that will be considered here.

The most striking clinical feature of malaria is a high fever which, in two common forms at least, has a characteristic periodicity. The condition thus recognized was well known to the ancients. The association of this disease with certain unhealthy locations, particularly marshes, was also firmly established at an early period and fully confirmed by the experience of centuries. At the beginning of the nineteenth century little more was known about malaria. It was fairly readily diagnosed (although for many years to come often confused with the other fevers) and it was associated with marshes—probably the bad air, " malaria ", of these localities. One other fact was known: that true malaria was rapidly cured on the administration of cinchona bark.

The first 80 years of the nineteenth century added relatively little to man's knowledge of the disease except that morbid anatomists were able to point to a characteristic pathological feature of the disease—the presence of a brownish pigment in the tissues. This brownish tint to the spleen, liver and brain particularly had been noted by most pathologists who had conducted autopsies on cases of malaria—for example Lancisi and Annesley—but it was Meckel, in 1847, who pointed out that the pigmented condition of the organs was dependent upon the accumulation of pigment in the blood. This was confirmed by several workers including Virchow and Frierichs. However, the " melanaemia ", as it was now called, was not usually regarded as a characteristic feature of malaria alone. This malarial pigment is chiefly of importance in that it formed the starting point of the researches of Alphonse Laveran and hence of our true understanding of the disease.

Alphonse Laveran was born in 1845 in Paris, the son of a distinguished French army doctor and a mother who came of an old military family. Heredity and family tradition guided Laveran into medicine and the army. He passed his youth following his father from one military post to another and at the age of 18 entered l'École du service de Santé Militaire at Strasbourg from which he graduated in 1867. He spent the next few months working in a number of military hospitals but with the outbreak of the Franco-Prussian War saw immediate active service with the army of the East. He was present at the battles of Gravelotte and Saint-Privat and then fell back on Metz where he organized a hospital in the Chambriere barracks. Metz was at once besieged by the German army and the horrors of septic and gangrenous wounds, rampant dysentery and typhoid were aggravated by the privations of the siege. After less than two months Metz was compelled to capitulate and Laveran suffered in the general humiliation of French arms. His personal period of detention was however short lived. Because he was a doctor he was allowed to return to France early in November where he served in the military hospital at Lille until the end of the war. The following spring found him in Paris during its revolutions serving at L'hôpital Saint-Martin. In 1874 he was appointed Professor agrégé des Maladies et Épidemies des armées—a position occupied previously by his father. Laveran taught particularly pathology and now began a life devoted to medical research and teaching. He was fortunate in that for over 20 years his military duties did not clash with his scientific ambitions, and indeed, provided him with the opportunity to make one of the most important discoveries in the history of medicine. In 1878 he was posted to Algeria where he discovered the parasite of malaria, as will be recounted later. In 1884 he was appointed professor of military hygiene at Val-de-Grâce which position he held for 10 years. This was the usual term of office for military professors and Laveran then received an administrative appointment which gave him no opportunities for research and so, in 1896, he retired from the army.

He immediately sought some place where he might continue his researches and was made welcome by Duclaux and Roux at the Pasteur Institute, where he worked in an honorary capacity. He shared a room with F. Mesnil with whom he collaborated. Laveran took up again the study of the pathogenic protozoa of man and animals, particularly those occurring in the blood, and he continued to take an interest in malaria. He was instrumental in founding a society for antimalarial work in Corsica and became its president. This organization did valuable antimalarial work in Corsica between 1902 and 1905. Laveran lent his aid to various other antimalarial schemes and took an active part in various international congresses. Whilst working at the Pasteur Institute he took considerable interest in trypanosomes and in 1904 published in collaboration with Mesnil, a monumental monograph on this group of parasites. In 1906 the Pasteur Institute bought a large property in the rue Falguière which was converted into laboratories. Laveran was allotted the second floor where he set up, personally donating 100,000 francs for the purpose, a laboratory for tropical medicine. In this commodious laboratory he worked almost to the day of his death.

His researches covered a wide area including bacteriology, experimental pathology and hygiene as well as protozoology. In 1908 he founded the Société de Pathologie Exotique and served as its president for 12 years. During the First World War he served on various committees concerned with the health of the army. Laveran received many honours both at home and abroad and in 1907 he received the Nobel prize for his work on protozoa as pathogenic agents. He was a foreign member of the Royal Societies of London and Edinburgh. He died after a short illness, the only illness which had ever interrupted his work, in 1922.

What of his character? Laveran is said to have been most industrious, which can readily be believed. A list of his publications occupies 89 pages and his books on malaria, trypanosomiasis, pathology and hygiene are all major works. His biographer, Marie Phisalix, claims that he was a man of simple and modest character but others found him self-opinionated and intolerant and his relations with some, at least, of his colleagues were not of the best.

But having briefly outlined the career of this great scientist we must go back to the year 1878 when his first term as professor at Val-de-Grâce had come to an end and the 33-year-old "médecin-major de 1re classe" was posted to Algeria, to the military hospital at Bone. Almost at once Laveran had the opportunity to conduct post-mortem examinations on a number of cases of acute, pernicious malaria and like others before him was struck by the pigmentation of the spleen, liver and brain which he recognized as characteristic of malaria. He examined microscopically a drop of blood taken from the spleen and found that besides an abundance of free pigment there were also leucocytes containing ingested pigment and also pigmented "hyaline bodies of irregular shape". The study of histological sections of all organs showed the presence of these pigmented elements in the blood within capillaries. The hyaline bodies were clearly different from the pigment containing leucocytes which could be well stained with carmine. Continuing his studies on the blood taken from living patients he noted in malarial blood two other bodies: a spherical hyaline corpuscle and also a very characteristic crescent-shaped body. Whilst still in doubt as to whether or not these were parasitic organisms he observed, on November 6th, 1880, in the blood of a 24-year-old artilleryman, at the edge of one of the spherical corpuscles several very actively moving filamentous bodies. He was no longer in doubt that here was a living parasite. Laveran lost no time in announcing his discovery in the form of a short note to a meeting of the Académie de Médecine in Paris on November 23rd. He followed this by a second note a month later.

During the following year Laveran collected observations on 192 patients with various forms of malaria and was able to demonstrate his parasite in 148 of them. He then published a full account of his studies in a monograph of 140 pages and as a report to the Académie des Sciences dated October 24th, 1881. Laveran now recognized four different forms of malaria parasite: a cylindrical element always curved like a crescent, transparent spherical bodies about the size of a red blood cell to which actively moving flagella were sometimes attached, another spherical element, motionless and containing pigment, and lastly another spherical element containing pigment, sometimes motile but of much smaller diameter—about 1/6 that of a red cell. These forms clearly corresponded to the female and male gametes, the rosette and the trophozoite *i.e.* all the main forms taken by the parasite in human blood. This work constituted no mean feat of observation for Laveran worked with a poor microscope of low magnifying power and with unstained preparations. E. Richard, a colleague of Laveran, stationed at Philipville, Algeria, was able to confirm all Laveran's observations and add two important points: that there was a very small form of the parasite which contained no pigment, as the youngest form, and that the parasites existed inside the red cells. Laveran thought them free or attached to the outside.

Laveran was, not unnaturally, anxious to confirm his observations on malarial patients in some other parts of the world. Accordingly in

1882 he went to Rome where excellent facilities and abundant malaria cases were to be found. He was allowed access to the San Spirito Hospital and was soon able to confirm his findings to his own satisfaction. But to convince the Roman medical profession was another matter. The *Bacillus malariae* of Klebs and Tommassi-Crudelli was regarded as the undoubted cause of malaria. E. Marchiafava was particularly sceptical of Laveran's work as were A. Celli and Tommassi-Crudelli himself. Although Laveran's actual observations could hardly be doubted, the Italian workers regarded the parasites as degenerative changes in the red cells. This was the view they held in 1884. However, in 1885 Marchiafava and Celli changed their minds and acknowledged the parasitic nature of Laveran's bodies.

At this point it will be convenient to deal, as a whole, with the main Italian contribution to our understanding of malaria. During the nineteenth century there was rather more overt jealousy over credit for work done than we see today and the Italian workers were never slow to claim their due in this respect. Italy boasted a number of enthusiastic and able students of malaria whose facilities for the study of the disease were probably unrivalled in the whole world. In Rome they had the University and hospitals of a capital city and the surrounding Campagna was one of the most malarious districts in the world. They had abundant patients and unrivalled opportunities for epidemiological and experimental studies. It is therefore surprising that, although their contribution to the subject was not negligible, it was relatively unimportant. This, perhaps, they felt themselves and it doubtless conditioned them to minimize the work of others and claim all that they could for themselves. The two cardinal discoveries in relation to malaria, the discovery of the parasite itself and the fact that it developed outside the human body in a mosquito entirely eluded them and were made by two army medical officers working in their spare time under primitive and even difficult circumstances.

The most significant Italian observations were made by Camillo Golgi of Pavia. Golgi was born in 1844, the son of a medical practitioner. He graduated from the University of Padua in 1865 and, influenced by the new cellular pathology of Virchow, worked under Bizzozero, the histologist. His circumstances forced him to take a position in a small hospital for incurables in 1872. But he carried on with his researches, despite disheartening conditions, and there he developed his famous silver-impregnation for staining the nervous system. In 1879 he was, for a year, professor of anatomy at Siena but the following year was appointed professor of histology and general pathology at Pavia. It was there, between 1886 and 1893, that he devoted much of his time to the study of malaria. In 1906 he was awarded the Nobel prize, not for his work on malaria but for his work on the structure of the nervous system. He died in 1926. Golgi in 1886 showed that there were two distinct species of malaria parasite. The one, the quartan parasite which completed its life-cycle in man in three days and the other, tertian, which completed its life-cycle in two days. These parasites he showed to be morphologically quite distinct: they differed in the degree of amoeboid movement, in effect on the size of the red cell, in type of pigment produced, and in the number of spores which developed in each red cell at sporulation. He also showed that the paroxysms of fever were related to the multiplication of the parasites in the blood stream. These observations did indeed mark an important advance.

This work was taken further by another prominent Italian student of malaria, Ettore Marchiafava with the assistance of Amigo Bignami. Marchiafava was born in 1847 and was educated and spent his working life in Rome where he became professor of pathological anatomy in 1882. Bignami was 15 years his junior and his lecturer in pathological anatomy. They utilized their excellent opportunities for epidemiological, clinical and pathological studies in Rome to study the natural history of the disease. They were able to show that, as well as the two types of malaria defined by Golgi, there was yet another and more important. The tertian and quartan malarias, they found, occurred throughout the whole year, in the winter and in spring being the only types seen. However, in summer and autumn, they were vastly outnumbered by cases which were clinically distinct, whose fever was less regular and which were much more severe and not infrequently fatal—a malignant malaria. The fever in these cases they thought to be either quotodian or tertian but the parasites causing the malignant tertian fevers were quite different from those causing the benign ones. They were smaller, had finer pigment granules, caused the red cells to shrink and produced fewer spores. This was another very important discovery and, as Marchiafava and Bignami pointed out, of great value in clinical prognosis. A patient with typical tertian fever but with the malignant type of parasite in his blood was at much greater risk than one with the benign tertian parasite. The malignant fevers were not always tertian, often being quotodian, and here Marchiafava and Bignami were led astray, describing yet another species of parasite distinct from the malignant tertian. The differences were not marked, and they admitted difficulty in distinguishing them, but nonetheless they were of the opinion that this fourth species did exist. This work constitutes the main contribution of Marchiafava and Bignami but they also published in 1894 a monograph on the *Summer-Autumn Malarial Fevers* which was translated for the New Sydenham Society and formed a useful contribution to the literature.

Meanwhile we must return to consider further the spread of what became derisively known in the Indian Medical Service as "Laveranity". Probably the earliest English-speaking convert was G. M. Sternberg, a major in the United States Army Medical Corps. In 1881 he had tried unsuccessfully to verify the claims of Klebs and Tommassi-Crudelli concerning the *Bacillus malariae* and courageously opposed their great authority. Whilst in Rome in 1885 Marchiafava had demonstrated the true malaria parasite to him and on his return to the United States he in his turn demonstrated the parasite in Welch's laboratory in the Johns Hopkins Hospital in March 1886. In 1887 W. T. Councilman, from Welch's laboratory, announced to the Pathological Society of Philadelphia the finding of flagellate parasites in 11 out of 80 attempts. Osler, speaking as he afterwards said, "in the fullness of his ignorance" was sceptical, regarding the so-called parasites as vacuoles in the red cells. On his return to Philadelphia however he at once set to work to find out the truth for himself. He was soon able to verify the existence of the parasites but was still cautious about assigning to them a causal role. By 1887 he was convinced and published an important paper on "The haematozoa of malaria" in which he discussed the nature of the parasite and compared it with other known haematozoa. From this time on, after its slow beginning, the doctrine of "Laveranity" was rapidly confirmed in many parts of the world. The parasites were found in India by van Dyke Carter working at Grant Medical College. Carter, who had come out to India in 1855, was one of the ablest and most indefatigable of Indian pathologists. His results, published in 1888, fully confirmed Laveran's findings. Metchinikoff and others found the parasites in Russia, Morado and Coronado in Havana, Anderson in Mauritius, Atkinson in Hong Kong and, more interesting since in a temperate climate, Quinke in Kiel.

Thus by 1890 Laveran's parasites were accepted the world over as the cause of malaria but it had taken 10 years—a not inconsiderable gestation period. It should also be noted that the disease had been transmitted experimentally from man to man by inoculation of blood from a malaria patient into a healthy person. This was probably first achieved by Gerhardt in 1882, although he was ignorant of the existence of the parasite, and was certainly convincingly demonstrated by Marchiafava in 1885.

A good starting point for a study of the development of our knowledge of the method of transmission of the malaria parasite is to examine the views held by Laveran in 1891. During the 11 years which had elapsed since his discovery of the parasite Laveran had been a keen student of all aspects of the disease and had given particular attention to this obviously important facet of the problem. His ideas on the subject may be fairly summarized as follows: Firstly, he regarded the association of malaria with marshy ground as absolutely established. The disease was also more frequent in warmer climates and generally fell into abeyance during the winter. Altitude also seemed to be of importance. He noted that experience had long ago led the populations of malarious areas to retire, if geographically possible, to mountains during the fever season. His own experience attested to the soundness of this move, for, in the higher parts of Constantine and Bone malaria was much less common than in the lower parts of the town. The most likely modes of transmission seemed to Laveran to be spread via water, via air or possibly by mosquitoes. Of these possibilities, whilst he admitted that, in fact, the answer was not known, he favoured spread by water. Laveran searched for the parasite outside the body, examining samples of soil and water from malarious areas. He, of course, found amoeboid organisms but was not convinced that any were in fact malaria parasites. He quoted the work of Grassi and Feletti who had found encysted amoebae in the nasal cavities of pigeons which had been placed in a malarious locality, and who later were found to have parasites in the blood, but he regarded the morphological resemblances of these bodies with the malaria parasite as incomplete. Although spread by water was the mode of transmission favoured by Laveran, he certainly considered the possibility of the disease being mosquito-borne but made no practical observations of this point himself. He stated that it seemed probable to him that the malaria parasite existed as a parasite of some other animal or plant, and he was well aware that the blood of birds contained very similar parasites. Mosquitoes were always abundant in malarious areas and drainage concomitantly eradicated both mosquitoes and malaria. He knew that filaria underwent development in the mosquito and that Findlay thought that mosquitoes transmitted yellow fever in Havana. These facts he quoted as possibly relevant to the problem of malarial infection but went no further.

Mannaberg, in a scholarly review of malaria published in 1893, added nothing to the views of Laveran although differing from him in detail. Julius Mannaberg of Vienna spent the summers of 1890, 1891 and 1892 studying the disease in malarious areas of Istria, Dalmatia, Croatia and Slavonia, then part of the Austro-Hungarian monarchy. Mannaberg regarded Laveran's supposition about mosquitoes as completely disproved by some negative experiments made by Grassi. However, the repeated failure of many investigators to find the malaria parasite in a free-living form led him to conclude that it must exist as a parasite of some other animal or plant. He regarded it as undoubted that malaria germs could be inhaled with the air and was inclined to discount spread by water.

Thus it can be said that in 1894 the mode of transmission of malaria parasites was quite unknown but that informed opinion favoured spread by air or water. However, in that year work began which was to lead to the correct solution of the problem four years later and this course of investigation must now be considered. In March 1894

Surgeon-major Ronald Ross of the Indian Medical Service arrived in England on leave. He was 38 years old and had been interested in malaria for a few years. He had examined the blood of malaria patients looking, without success, for Laveran's parasites about which he was sceptical. On his arrival in London Ross went to discuss the matter with Professor Kanthack at St. Bartholomew's Hospital who assured him that Laveran's work was sound and referred him to Manson. Ross first met Manson on April 10th and within a few minutes Manson had demonstrated malarial " crescents " in a stained film to Ross's entire satisfaction. Ross called on Manson again in November and on this occasion, whilst walking down Oxford Street together, Manson propounded his theory that malaria was transmitted by mosquitoes. Ross was familiar with the hypothesis, having seen it mentioned in Laveran's book. However, Manson's theory was more tangible, more verifiable, for he suggested that it was the motile filaments which developed when malarial blood was shed which were the elements concerned in this extra corporeal development. He postulated that the flagellate bodies were a kind of spore which passed through the wall of the mosquito's stomach and underwent further development in a manner unknown. With this argument Ross was " immensely impressed ". He determined to test the hypothesis on his return to India.

Meanwhile Manson published an account of his views in the *British Medical Journal* in December 1894 in a paper entitled " On the nature and significance of the crescents and flagellated bodies in malarial blood ". Manson reasoned thus: clearly the human blood stream was the natural habitat for the malaria parasite, therefore there must be some arrangement for the entry and egress of the parasites. As in a malarious patient there was no physiological nor pathological mechanism whereby blood could escape from the body, how did the parasites get out? The problem facing the malaria parasite was, in every way, similar to that facing the filaria larva. He therefore suggested that " the solution of the problem may be the same for both ". Moreover, he was able to postulate a mechanism. He drew attention to the significance of the flagellate bodies, always found in malaria blood, but never immediately after its withdrawal. Since these bodies did not apparently exist in the circulating blood they must be " intended to carry on the life of the species outside the human body". Reasoning, as always, like a naturalist and drawing on his knowledge of comparative parasitology, he also suggested that since the malaria parasite is an intracellular parasite in man "like a gregarine or a coccidium" it was "probable that outside the human body it retains this habit". Manson concluded by saying that "It would be idle to attempt to follow the parasite without the assistance of direct observations . . . But the hypothesis I have ventured to formulate seems so well grounded that I for one, did circumstances permit, would approach its experimental demonstration with confidence". He commended the problem to medical officers serving in India and other malarious areas. It was this idea and none other, incomplete and only partially accurate as it is, that stimulated and guided Ross to the solution.

At this point it will be convenient to consider a remarkable paper by Dr. Albert Freeman Africanus King. King was born in Oxfordshire in 1841, the son of a doctor who emigrated to the United States when his son was 10 years old. He studied medicine at the National Medical College of Washington, qualifying in 1861. After the civil war he settled in Washington and was present in Ford's theatre the night that President Lincoln was assassinated. He gave the wounded president first aid and helped carry him across the street to the house in which he died. King specialized in obstetrics, of which subject he was professor in the George Washington University and in the University of Vermont, and wrote a very popular *Manual of Obstetrics.* He died in 1914. His paper on the epidemiology of malaria was read to the Philosophical Society of Washington as early as February 1882 and published in the *Popular Science Monthly* in September of the next year. It is a masterpiece of fundamental epidemiological observation and reasoning. King was aware of the work of Manson implicating mosquitoes as vectors of Filaria, of Carolos Finlay's hypothesis that yellow fever was carried by mosquitoes and of the fact that some cases of that type of anthrax known as malignant pustule were caused by the bite of horse-flies. King realized that many of the well-attested observations on the epidemiology of malaria could be explained on the supposition that the disease was carried by mosquitoes—far better explained, in fact, than transmission via air. Thus the association with marshes where mosquitoes breed, the necessity for the ambient temperature to be above 60 degrees Fahrenheit, and the complete abolition of malaria if the temperature fell to 32 degrees, fitted well with the known breeding habits of mosquitoes. Likewise the barrier offered by a belt of trees, but the danger of that tree belt itself could be readily explained on the basis of a mosquito vector. The danger of exposure to the night air in malarious areas, the advent of malaria when the soil was dug over and pools suitable for mosquitoes to breed in produced, the reduction of malaria when marshes were drained, its relative infrequency in towns or above a certain altitude could all be admirably explained by his hypothesis. In one particular respect King's hypothesis was a great advance on Manson's for he specifically suggested that malaria was transmitted by the bite of mosquitoes whereas Manson thought that the germs of malaria were liberated into water on the death of the mosquito. King's paper is indeed remarkable from the scientific point of view and an admirable piece of epidemiological reasoning in the classic style. However, the historians' admiration must be tinged with regret and even censure that, having gone so far, King went no further. His publication was in a journal that would have scant circulation in the medical world and it does seem to be a fact that none of the workers on malaria ever saw it. Moreover, King was well placed to follow up his hypothesis experimentally. Malaria was common around Washington. Because he displayed no more initiative his valuable paper was quite without influence in solving the great malaria problem and has only been resurrected by historians long after Ross had, quite independently, proved King's suppositions true. Of the other malaria researchers who had given thought to the possibility of mosquitoes acting as a vector there was Laveran who, we have seen, did nothing about it, and also G. B. Grassi who claimed considerable credit for the establishment of this truth and whose claims will be examined later.

We must now return to Surgeon-major Ross who, on March 28th 1895, embarked for India leaving his wife and family behind. In his *Memoirs,* published in 1923, Ross has left a wonderful account of his part in the discovery of the life-cycle of the malaria parasite. He conveys the moods of excitement, disappointment, frustration and triumph with the dramatic skill of the poet and novelist that he was. But, wisely, he allows the story largely to tell itself, by giving extensive quotations from a long series of letters written by him to Manson at that time. The historian cannot possibly do better than to follow his example. Ross lost no time in setting to work. The crew and passengers on the P. & O. steamship *Ballarat* were screened for malaria cases but without success. However, he obtained practice in the use of his new microscope and in dissection by looking for parasites in cockroaches and in flying-fish. He also read such literature on malaria as he had been able to obtain. Ross arrived at his regiment at Secunderabad on April 24th, established himself in a bungalow with Captain Thomas and Lieutenant Hole, " both first-rate fellows " and " after paying the usual ceremonial calls . . . got to work at once in the best of health and spirits ". Unfortunately malaria cases were not common at this season, but, within a few days he had located some patients and demonstrated the parasite in their blood. Unfortunately some of his colleagues were less than helpful; one would not allow Ross to experiment on his patients and the principal medical officer put him on "every duty conceivable". However, malaria cases were obtained from the bazaar, mosquitoes bred from larvae, initial technical difficulties overcome and on May 13th—his birthday—he made his first significant observation. Manson had postulated that the flagellate forms were spores, adapted for life outside the human body, and these, in turn, were derived from a characteristic, cresent-shaped, form of the parasite in the blood. It was these crescents upon which Ross concentrated his observation. He found that they rapidly altered when blood was taken into the mosquito's stomach—they became spherules. Although this happened in control blood samples merely sealed on glass slide under a coverslip, it happened much more rapidly and completely in the mosquito stomach, suggesting that this might be the natural site for the transformation. On May 23rd he was able to report to Manson, on the basis of a study of 28 mosquitoes fed on malaria blood, " that the stomach of the mosquito is very probably the natural locus for the crescent-spherule-flagella metamorphosis ". Ross added, " I look upon these observations to be as much yours as if you had made them ". By May 28th he had studied 54 mosquitoes, dissecting them at intervals after feeding and so following the whole process of crescent-spherule-flagella metamorphosis. He had also, meanwhile, tried to infect a volunteer by feeding him water containing the eggs of a mosquito previously fed on malarial blood. His volunteer developed a slight fever but after following his temperature for some weeks and repeatedly examining his blood for parasites, with negative results, Ross realized that he was on a false trail. He returned to " follow the flagellum ". On July 18th he spent three hours watching the process of exflagellation in the contents of a mosquito's stomach, which he described graphically in a letter to Manson, and concluded by saying that he regarded the " first step " as completely proved.

However, Ross had not been able to follow the flagellum into the tissues of the mosquito, as Manson's hypothesis predicted, and so, about the beginning of August, he adopted a new approach which was entirely his own idea. He kept mosquitoes alive for several days after being fed and then searched their bodies, micron by micron, under the microscope for parasites of any kind. He proposed then to try to correlate these with malaria parasites. Almost immediately he came upon a species of gregarine which he thought fell in wonderfully with Manson's idea of an alternative form. " You can imagine my excitement over all this—though it may turn out to be a wrong scent ", he wrote to Manson. Throughout August Ross worked at the life-cycle of this gregarine and thought that " this psorosperm theory is looking very promising ". He had also been keeping a record of malaria parasites found in cases of fever. Out of 110 cases examined he had found the parasite in 65, amply confirming its diagnostic value.

At the beginning of September his malaria work received the first of its interruptions. He was posted to Bangalore on special sanitary duty, to help fight a cholera epidemic. Although this interruption was to last for 18 months Ross did not resent it. The work of combating the epidemic and of saving human life appealed to his practical nature. (He always regarded his great discovery as of importance mainly because it showed the way to eradicate malaria.) The experience in sanitary work proved valuable and he was able to do some malaria work. He tried to infect men by getting them to drink water containing his psorosperms but with negative results. But his mind was moving on, and on May 27th, 1896, in a letter to Manson, he wrote, " the belief is growing on me that the disease is communicated by the bite of the mosquito. What do you think? " Ross tried getting mosquitoes which had fed " immediately before " to bite a volunteer but again with a negative result. Manson thought this idea interesting but did not favour it,

Ross had already published some of his results, but in Indian journals with probably little European circulation. His work may therefore have been unknown to others interested in malaria, particularly the Italian workers. However, in March 1896, Manson delivered the Goulstonian lectures before the Royal College of Physicians in London, describing his hypothesis and Ross's work to that date. These lectures were published in the *British Medical Journal* in March 1896 and Ross's work thus far must be presumed to have become well known to any serious student of malaria. One of the Italians, A. Bignami, published a paper in July 1896 objecting to Manson's theory and stating that the process of exflagellation was in fact the death struggles of the malaria parasite. Ross was able to disprove this suggestion by showing that it did not occur in sealed preparations of blood on a slide. Ross himself published an account of his work in the *British Medical Journal* of January 30th, 1897.

At the end of March, his sanitary work at Bangalore finished, Ross took leave at Ootacammund where he was joined by his wife and family. Meanwhile, failure to detect any further development of the parasite beyond the exflagellation stage had led Ross to doubt if the species of mosquito which he was using for his experiments (later identified as species of *Culex* and *Stegomyia*) were malaria-bearing species. He thought this in October 1896 and wrote to Manson " I have lately been thinking that the first thing necessary for further investigations is to be sent to a place where I can be pretty sure that the species of mosquitoes is a malaria-bearing one ". His leave at Ootacammund offered an opportunity to study the disease in just such an area, for although at Ootacammund, 8,000 feet above sea level, there was no malaria, the disease abounded in valleys only half an hour's ride on a bicycle from his house. He began his investigations in one of these valleys, Sigur Ghat, in April. Malaria certainly existed amongst workers on a local tea plantation. His work was, however, brought suddenly to an end on April 25th when he himself went down with malaria, probably acquired earlier in the month. He promptly dosed himself with quinine and although far from well continued his search for different species of mosquitoes. During the first two weeks of May he spent his days mosquito hunting and on the 10th an intelligent native brought him five specimens of a type he had not seen before. This type did not frequent houses but was common in the neighbouring jungle. They were small with brindled bellies and contained swarms of psorosperms. He was elated! He wrote to Manson " Culex Sylvestris has entirely altered the state of affairs. Where I was just about to give up the theory owing to the absence of mosquitoes I found that mosquitoes are swarming. If then malaria occupies the mosquito at all it occupies the Culex Sylvestris ". But this was yet another false trail for this species, in fact, does not carry malaria.

Still on leave, he continued to follow his method of searching mosquitoes for any parasite which might be a stage in the life-cycle of the malaria parasite, discovering in the course of this work five new species of parasites. Ross by now realized that he was " up against a very difficult problem indeed—an equation containing two unknown quantities. There were many species of mosquitoes, and each of these contained many kinds of parasites. How was I to discover which species of mosquito and which kind of parasite were the right ones?".

Ross was now 40 years old and had seen 16 years' service. The authorities had taken no notice of his malaria work, had given him neither leave nor facilities, and he felt very dispirited. After two years of work, promising though his results had been, he seemed to have reached an impasse. He saw himself condemned for the rest of his service to regimental work at the lowest salary for his rank. He therefore determined to retire on his first pension, which would be due in a year, but first he braced himself for " one more desperate effort to solve the Great Problem ". He rejoined his regiment, the 19th Madras Infantry, on the 18th June, 1897, leaving his family at Ootacammund. Almost immediately he was stricken with a severe attack of food poisoning, possibly cholera (there was one fatal case in the outbreak), acquired at a mess dinner. He indited a report on his malaria work to the Director-General hoping to get seconded for special duty. After his severe labour at Ootacammund he felt a " violent reaction against the microscope " and could hardly bring himself to look through it for a month. The monsoon appeared to have failed and the heat and dust seemed unbearable. He wrote:

> What ails the solitude?
> Is this the Judgment day?
> The sky is red as blood;
> The very rocks decay
> And crack and crumble, and
> There is a flame of wind
> Wherewith the burning sand
> Is ever mass'd and thin'd.

Then the thought struck him: " Why not see whether mosquitoes fed on malarial blood as before contain any of the mosquito-parasites which I had found in the Sigur Ghat? I was at full work again on 21st July, 1897 on the last lap ".

His principle of work was, as he wrote to Manson, as follows: " I am of course sticking to the flagellulae again but on a slightly modified principle. Owing to their extreme delicacy I doubt whether they can be directly followed into the insect tissues; but this difficulty can be avoided in a simple manner. The question I have set myself to answer, and which I now feel able to tackle, is " Do healthy mosquitoes fed on malarial blood, contain any parasite which similar mosquitoes fed on normal blood do not contain? . . . I keep mosquitoes, after feeding on crescents, for one, two, three . . . days and then examine, so as to allow the flagellulae time, by supposition, to mature into full-grown mosquito-parasites . . . suspicious bodies being noted, I have only to compare with control insects . . . ".

Ross must be allowed to tell his own story: " But the weather became very hot again in August. At first I toiled comfortably, but as failure followed failure, I became exasperated and worked till I could hardly see my way home late in the afternoons. Well do I remember that dark hot little office in the hospital at Begumpett, with the necessary gleam of light coming in from under the eaves of the veranda. I did not allow the punka to be used because it blew about my dissected mosquitoes, which were partly examined without a cover glass; and the result was that swarms of ' eye-flies '—minute little insects which try to get into one's ears and eyelids—tormented me at their pleasure, while an occasional Stegomyia revenged herself on me for the death of her friends. The screws of my microscope were rusted with sweat from my forehead and hands, and its last remaining eye-piece was cracked ". Writing to his wife he said: " I have failed in finding parasites in mosquitoes fed on malaria patients, but perhaps am not using the proper kind of mosquitoes ".

But now " some Angel Fate " had put into the hands of one of his " mosquito-men " some larvae, which hatched out a different, dappled mosquito, a single specimen of which Ross had seen in Sigur Ghat. On August 16th these were fed on his malaria patient, Husein Khan. That evening he wrote to his wife: " I have found another kind of mosquito with which I am now experimenting, and hope for more satisfactory results with it ". On the 17th he dissected two of these mosquitoes but found nothing unusual. On the 19th he killed another and found " some peculiar vacuolated cells in the stomach about 10 microns in diameter ". He thought little about them and was rather disheartened at his results with the new species. On August 20th, a dull, hot day, Ross went to the hospital at 7 a.m., examined his patients, dealt with his correspondence and had a hurried breakfast in the mess. One of his mosquitoes had died and this he dissected without noting anything significant. He had two mosquitoes left of the batch fed on Husein Khan on the 16th and at about 1 p.m. he determined to sacrifice one. Dissecting it he scrutinized the tissues micron by micron, when suddenly, in the stomach wall he " saw a clear and almost perfectly circular outline before me of about 12 microns in diameter. The outline was much too sharp, the cell too small to be an ordinary stomach-cell of a mosquito. I looked a little further. Here was another and another exactly similar cell ". He changed the focus of his microscope and there within each of these new cells was a cluster of black pigment. He made rough drawings in his notebook, sealed his specimen, went home to tea and slept solidly for an hour. The pigment puzzled him, for the flagella contained no pigment, but the thought struck him that if the cells were really parasites they should grow in size in the last remaining mosquito during the night. He spent the night in agony lest his last remaining mosquito should die and decompose before morning. Next day he slew and dissected, with shaking hand, this remaining specimen. "There were the cells again, twenty-one of them, just as before, only now much larger . . . The cells were therefore parasites, and, as they contained the characteristic malarial pigment, were almost certainly the malaria parasites growing in the mosquito's tissues. The thing was really done . . . ".

Next morning, after writing to his wife, Ross scribbled in a notebook:

> This day designing God
> Hath put into my hand
> A wonderous thing. And God
> Be praised. At his command
> I have found thy secret deeds
> Oh million-murdering Death.
>
> I know that this little thing
> A million men will save—
> Oh death where is thy sting?
> Thy victory oh grave?

All this he reported soberly in a letter to Manson dated August 22nd, 1897. Ross had, still, a long way to go before the life-cycle of the malaria parasite was worked out but the great significance of his discovery on August 20th—Mosquito Day, as he ever after called it—was that he had shown that the malaria parasite went through further development in the mosquito tissues, beyond the crescent-spherule-flagella transformation, which occurred, at least to some degree, on a microscope slide.

Immediately following these discoveries his work was held up by shortage of dappled-winged mosquitoes and on 4th September he joined his family at Bangalore for 10 days leave. He made it his first task to write a paper "On some peculiar pigmented cells found in two mosquitoes fed on malarial blood". The article appeared in print in the *British Medical Journal* on December 18th, 1897.

Meanwhile he returned to Secunderabad and after some delay obtained a supply of mosquitoes bred from the larvae. He confidently expected to be able to work out the whole cycle within a fortnight—but then the blow fell with the following order: "Under instructions from Command Headquarters Surgeon-Major R. Ross I.M.S., will proceed immediately to Bombay for military duty ". The Tirah campaign against the Afrides had begun. Ross did not however go on active service. After some delays he was posted to the pretty little station of Kherwara where there was nothing to do. Ross thought, perhaps with reason, that he was being deliberately persecuted, and to have his work interrupted at such a stage was hard indeed. However the four and a half months spent in Kherwara were not without benefit. He was able to relax, and a rest he undoubtedly needed. He fished and shot, and although there was no malaria in Kherwara, he examined the blood of frogs, toads, fishes and birds. On December 14th he came across a parasite, *Halteridium,* in the red cells of a blue-rock pigeon. He shot more birds finding *Halteridium* common, but in pigeons only. They were also present in the blood of tame pigeons and in the blood in the stomachs of the mosquitoes which plagued them. This *Halteridium,* which was discovered by Danilewsky in 1886, was an intracellular parasite of the red cells of birds and was not unlike the malaria parasite. This was Ross's first acquaintance with this parasite and, as will be seen later, was to be important in the working out of the complete life-cycle of the malaria parasite. So that vexatious as Ross found his " punishment " at Kherwara, the interlude was not without use to him.

In January 1898, the Tirah expedition having come to an end, Ross received the joyful news, by telegram, that the government had sanctioned his secondment for special duty for six months. He was to report to Calcutta where the laboratory of Lieutenant Colonel Cunningham, F.R.S., a distinguished I.M.S. officer, and professor of physiology was put at his disposal. It was early March before he was able to settle down to work. Cases of malaria were scarce. He tried various types of mosquitoes on such cases as he could obtain, but he also decided, now, to work with the parasites of bird red cells as well.

In February 1898 Manson had drawn Ross's attention to a most interesting discovery made by W. G. MacCallum, a medical student at Johns Hopkins Hospital, whilst working with *Halteridium.* MacCallum described the process of conjugation between the flagellate body and granular bodies. They were male and female gametes. Manson had at once grasped the significance of this observation in relation to malaria and wrote to Ross that if the male element " is a fertilizing factor in the halteridium cycle then the flagellated body of malaria is also a fertilizing factor in the plasmodium cycle ".

Because of the difficulties in getting human cases of malaria Ross set to work hard on birds, but initially in a confused manner, feeding various mosquitoes on sparrows, larks, pigeons and crows. All his dissections were negative except one which showed two pigmented cells, but he did not know which bird this mosquito had bitten, In recording this in a letter to Manson he added, " Am pretty well dead beat . . . ". Pulling himself together Ross set out to determine the origin of the pigment cells. By experiment he was able to eliminate the crows and pigeons and on examining the blood of larks and sparrows carefully, which he had not done before, he found another type of intracellular parasite—*Proteosoma*. Had the pigment cells come from there?

On the night of March 17th he fed grey mosquitoes on three *Proteosoma* infected larks. On the morning of the 20th he judged these mosquitoes to be ready and was so excited, that at 8 a.m., he could hardly dissect the first one. It contained pigment cells, as did five out of nine of the mosquitoes. Ross " felt that the theory was proved ". He wrote to Manson, " of course I have only to find sporulation to complete the life history ". The difficulty was to keep the mosquitoes alive long enough. After another week's work he had found that the pigmented cells increased steadily in size, about the fourth day lost their pigment and began to protrude through the stomach wall into the body cavity of the mosquito. At this stage he thought sporulation ought to take place but was puzzled by the fact that at about six days the cells seemed to burst and disappear. Early April he spent confirming his findings and extending them in a quantitative way. Out of 15 mosquitoes fed on healthy sparrows not a single one developed the peculiar type of cell—" coccidium ", he called it. Of 19 fed on a sparrow whose blood contained only a few *Proteosoma* all contained coccidia and out of 20 fed on a sparrow with numerous *Proteosoma* all contained numerous coccidia. As many as 40 per high power microscope field! On April 5th he wrote to Manson: " Thus at one stroke we get the law:—the number of coccidia in the mosquito is proportioned to the number of parasites in the blood of the birds . . . What a beautiful discovery this is! I can venture to praise it because it belongs to you, not me. I sometimes think it is the prettiest thing in the whole range of pathology . . . of course its discovery implies the solution of the malaria problem . . . ".

He now wished to enlarge the scope of operations and go to Terai, near Darjeeling, where there was malaria. But leave to travel had to be obtained first. Why did not Ross immediately work to complete the life-cycle of *Proteosoma*? This surely was the first task, and in retrospect Ross must have felt so too. But he excused himself on the grounds that he had to write a report of work done, so that his six months special duty might be extended, that he wanted to work with human malaria and lastly that he was suffering from overwork and heat. On April 17th he left Calcutta with his wife, his two native assistants and numbers of cages of birds—" to the utter amazement of the railway passengers"—and settled near Darjeeling where he wrote his report for the government entitled " Report on the cultivation of *Proteosoma,* Labbe, in grey Mosquitoes ", but otherwise wasted time. In his letters to Manson he reiterated that he regarded the problem as solved—all else was detail. Since Ross required government permission to publish results he got Manson to publish results of the work in the *British Medical Journal* of June 18th. He also agitated to be put on parasitological work on a more permanent basis pointing out that " as my pension is due in three weeks I feel pretty independent ".

He was back in Calcutta by the 4th of June admitting to Manson that he had " lost time in going to the Terai ". His first experiments were attempts to infect birds by feeding them infected mosquitoes but he soon returned to observing the developing " coccidia ". By chance he tried making his preparations in fairly strong salt solution which brought out very clearly a striated appearance in the mature " coccidia ". He realized that the cysts were full of " germinal threads 10 microns in length which are scattered into the living insect's coelom ". He stained them and found chromatin granules about their middles. What was the nature of these bodies? Perhaps spermatozoa, falciform bodies or a naked spore, he postulated to Manson.

Strain was beginning to tell on Ross. He wrote: "But this climate! I can perhaps stand another month of it. It is hell simply; and the constant strain on eye and mind at this temperature is making me thoroughly ill. If I cannot infect birds or find a clear opening by the end of July, I must clear out". Few research workers have struggled to finish an important piece of work under such conditions as Ross endured in July 1898. Dissecting infected mosquitoes he noted that some of the rod-shaped bodies "lay among the scales and muscles of the thorax and showed no further development. This scarcely looks like the spermatozoa theory".

On July 6th he wrote to Manson: "I feel almost justified in saying that I have completed the life-cycle of proteosoma, or rather one life-cycle of proteosoma, and therefore in all probability of the malaria parasite". He went on to explain that the "germinal threads" were in the blood of the mosquito and were actually "more numerous in the thorax than in the abdomen . . . sometimes rods were more common in the head . . .". They were particularly numerous in and near a gland in the front of the thorax—the salivary gland!

"I feel that I am almost entitled to lay down the law by direct observation and tracking the parasite step by step—Malaria is conveyed from a diseased person or bird to a healthy one by the proper species of mosquito, and is inoculated by its bite". He was soon able to show that the bite of infected mosquitoes did in fact transmit *Proteosoma* to uninfected birds. "One single experiment with crescents (there are numerous dappled winged mosquitoes here now) will enable me to bring human malaria into line with proteosoma—they are sure to be just the same", he wrote to Manson on July 9th. All this work Manson announced to the section of Tropical Diseases of the British Medical Association on July 28th and the work was published in the *Lancet, Journal of Tropical Medicine* and *British Medical Journal* all within a few weeks.

There can be no doubt that July 28th, 1898 should be taken as the date by which it was demonstrated to the world at large that the malaria-like parasite of birds, *Proteosoma,* developed in the mosquito and was transmitted to healthy birds by the bite of the mosquito. Ross's work had shown that human malaria parasites also went through a similar development in the appropriate species of mosquito. He had not actually followed the development of the human parasites further than the stomach wall of the mosquito nor had he transmitted malaria to man by the bite of an infected mosquito but there was no doubt that this could readily be done. This is, therefore, the date, July 28th, 1898, of the announcement to the world of the discovery of the method, until then unknown, of how malaria is transmitted from man to man. No work published after this date can possibly be considered as having priority over that of Ronald Ross.

But that "single experiment with crescents"—Ross never did it. When he had been granted six months special duty the investigation of kala-azar had been optimistically added to his malaria work by the authorities. This, he wrote, "weighs on me like a nightmare". Again, to Manson on August 11th: "I am dead beat and have asked leave to go to Kurseong for a few weeks en route for Assam. I have lost eleven pounds in weight the last two months. Work at the microscope all night; can't sleep; and feel as low as possible". He left Calcutta on the 13th and again, in his letter to Manson, complained of his poor health which had compelled him to stop even thinking about his malaria work. Ross remained in India a further six months. His official duty was to investigate kala-azar and try as he might he could not get excused this work. Nevertheless he continued to take an interest in malaria, correspond with Manson and others, dissect mosquitoes rather at random and demonstrate his results to C. W. Daniels, sent out by the Royal Society to verify Ross's results. He seems to have made no attempt to do that last crucial experiment. Ross needed to get some of his dappled winged mosquitoes, feed them on a patient with crescents in the blood, keep his mosquitoes alive some 10 to 20 days and then allow them to bite a healthy volunteer. Even this, simple as it sounds, would not have been without its difficulties. Acquiring the correct mosquito larvae, a suitable case of malaria and keeping his fed mosquitoes alive all presented problems, but it is hard to believe that a whole-hearted effort for three months would not have been crowned with success. In later life Ross was inclined to grumble that others had forestalled him in his final step, and to blame the imposed kala-azar investigation and the lack of help from the authorities. But he was in a position to ignore kala-azar and get on with his malaria work. In reality he seems to have regarded the work as done, the problem solved, and was disinclined to make the final effort. For this attitude, no doubt, the months of labour under most trying climatic conditions must be blamed. There was yet another reason why Ross failed to round off his work with human malaria. Ross was relatively uninterested in the purely scientific aspects of his work. His primary object was to save lives, to forestall "million-murdering death". Once he had shown that the malaria parasite spends a part of its life-cycle in the mosquito the way was open to prevent malaria by destroying mosquitoes. This fact Ross had demonstrated, to his satisfaction on "Mosquito Day" August the 20th, 1897—all subsequent work was, to Ross, filling in detail.

The credit for confirming that the human *Plasmodium* passed through the same stages of development in man as the *Proteosoma* in birds and was transmitted by the bite of the mosquito, as Ross had postulated, must go to a group of Roman workers, particularly A. Bignami and Grassi. Bignami seems to have early suspected that malaria might be transmitted by the bite of a mosquito, as indeed had Laveran and King. He claimed to have attempted to transmit the disease in this way by liberating mosquitoes from a malarious area into a room containing a volunteer in 1894. This somewhat crude approach yielded negative results and Bignami did not, at the time, report them. Two years later, stimulated by Manson's exposition of the mosquito theory in his Goulstonian lectures, Bignami reviewed the various theories on malaria and drew attention to the possibility that mosquitoes might inoculate the parasites into man. In support of this he pointed out that experimental inoculation with malarial blood, in minute quantities, produced the disease and Smith and Kilborne had already shown that the parasite of Texas fever was transmitted by the bite of ticks.

No further contributions of significance were made by the Italian workers until long after Ross had published, at the end of 1897, his article showing that malaria crescents went through development in the stomach wall of certain species of mosquitoes—the type of mosquito and its characteristic form of egg being inexpertly, but adequately, described. However, during the summer of 1898 Grassi began his investigations. Grassi was at that time 44 years old and professor of comparative anatomy in Rome. He was a very hard worker, a trained zoologist and amongst other distinguished contributions had helped to unravel the mysteries of the life-cycle of the eel. Grassi had, besides the advantages of his position, a good knowledge of mosquitoes. By laboriously collecting mosquitoes in the Campagna and correlating species with known malarious areas he was able to point the finger of suspicion at three species of mosquito which might carry malaria, whilst exonerating some 30 other species. These views he announced in October 1898 and the following month was able to transmit malaria to a volunteer by the bite of one of those species—*Anopheles claviger*.

By the end of 1898 Grassi and Bignami had followed the development of the malaria parasite from its site in the stomach wall of the mosquito, where Ross had left it, and show that it developed through to the stage of sporozoites in the salivary glands in exactly the same way as *Proteosoma*. Grassi always claimed not to have seen Ross's article in the *British Medical Journal* of December 1897 in which he described the development of the malaria parasites in a mosquito which was recognizably described as an *Anopheles*. Such negligence hardly redounds to his credit as a research worker but it was in fact the opinion of no less an authority than G. F. Nuttall that Ross's description rather than Grassi's theory of "Limitation of suspected hosts" had guided Grassi to the right species of mosquito.

By the beginning of 1899 the knowledge gained from the experiments of Ross, Bignami and Grassi clearly indicated the way in which malaria might be avoided. Man should be able to remain healthy in a malarious area if only he avoided being bitten by Anopheline mosquitoes. The first attempts to test malaria prophylaxis on this basis were made in 1899 by Professor A. Celli. Celli, who was born in 1857, and who had worked under Tommassi-Crudelli in Rome was a life-long student of malaria, particularly of its epidemiology in the Campagna. He was also the first to prove that the malaria pigment is derived from haemoglobin. Celli provided a railway worker's hut in the Campagna with efficient mosquito screening and impressed upon the family of the worker the necessity of staying indoors from sunset to sunrise. For the first time the occupants of this hut remained healthy throughout the malaria season—except the husband whose duties took him outside at nights; he developed severe malaria.

Meanwhile Manson was anxious to convince the layman, particularly those with responsibility for the government of British colonies in the tropics, that scientific investigation had pointed the way to practical prevention of malaria. He therefore pressed for the semi-public experiment, or rather demonstration, showing the role of mosquitoes in transmission of malaria. He persuaded the Colonial Office to finance the erection, for £300, of a pine-wood hut with effective mosquito screens on the edge of an intensely malarious swamp in the Campagna. In this hut lived Drs. G. C. Low and L. W. Sambon, a Signor Terzi and an Italian servant from the 19th July to 19th October, 1900. The inhabitants moved about the countryside freely during the day making miscellaneous studies in natural history—they discovered a new piroplasm of cattle and a new species of mole—but at sunset retired to their hut and did not leave it until sunrise. They all remained perfectly healthy in the midst of the fever-stricken peasant population. The experiment was conducted with some publicity and during the daytime the experimenters received visits from many well-known physicians and politicians as well as King Umberto of Italy.

Grassi, despite his jealousy, cabled to Manson, "Assembled in British experimental hut, having witnessed perfect health experimenters amidst malaria-stricken inhabitants—Italian physicians congratulate Manson who first clearly formulated mosquito-malaria theory ". Having convincingly demonstrated that the avoidance of mosquito bites prevented malarial infection, again at Manson's instigation, a dramatic demonstration of the converse proposition, that the bite of the Anopheline mosquitoes did cause malaria, was arranged. Bignami and Bastianelli reared Anopheline mosquitoes from larvae, allowed them to bite a patient with benign tertian malaria and dispatched them in special gauze cages in the British Embassy bag to London. These mosquitoes were then allowed to bite Manson's eldest son and Mr. George Warren, a laboratory assistant, both of whom developed malaria about a fortnight later.

Thus we come to the end of our account of the purely parasitological aspects of the history of malaria as the twentieth century opened. Many further details remained to be filled in and the story of the application of these discoveries to the saving of human life on a grand scale is omitted here as being more germane to the history of preventive medicine.

Bibliographical Note

Of the vast literature on malaria and its history the writer has depended chiefly on the following works, each of which in turn will lead the enquiring reader further into this most fascinating topic.

1. Laveran, A. (1893). *Paludism*. London: New Sydenham Society.
2. *Two Monographs on Malaria and the Parasites of Malarial Fevers* (1894). New Sydenham Society.
3. Ross, R. (1923). *Memoirs*. John Murray.
4. Bloomfield, A. L. (1958). *A Bibliography of Internal Medicine—Communicable Diseases*, p. 341
5. Manson-Bahr, P. (1962). *Int. Rev. trop. Med.* 2, 329.
6. Nuttall, G. H. (1901). *Quart. J. micr. Sci.* *44*, 429.
7. Grassi, G. B. (1924). *Parasitology*, *16*, 360.

Chapter XIV

PARASITOLOGY ESTABLISHED

By about the 1860's the foundations of the science of parasitology had been well laid and it was appreciated that parasites were responsible for an important part of the diseases to which man and his domestic animals were subject. This, it should be noted, was some 20 years before the role of bacteria as a cause of disease was finally established.

Thus far the science had developed mainly in Europe through the works of medical men and naturalists, both professional and amateur. Despite the fact that many parasitologists held medical qualifications the development of the subject up to the middle of the nineteenth century forms, in reality, a part of the history of zoology. Many of the distinguished medically qualified parasitologists were holders of chairs of zoology or some other branch of natural history. Although there had been much speculation on the role of parasites as a cause of disease since ancient times, it was not until about 1860 that it was unequivocally demonstrated that animal parasites were responsible for such serious conditions as hydatid disease and trichinosis.

Moreover, by this time the common and important parasites which infest man in temperate climates had been discovered and their life-cycles worked out. Although there is no clear cut distinction between the medicine of the tropics and temperate regions—was not the amoeba of dysentery discovered in St Petersburg—many of the major advances in parasitology over the next half century were to come from workers in the tropics. These facts lend a character to the history of parasitology for the subject was, to an unusually great extent, developed by individuals working outside universities, often under very primitive conditions. Of the early European workers it is true such men as Rudolphi, von Siebold and Leuckart worked in great universities but

Göze was a country clergyman, Kuchenmeister a general practitioner and Cobbold an independent gentleman never holding an academic position of great importance. The major discoveries in the tropical phase of parasitology were made by men even more isolated from the world of academic science; Army officers like Laveran in Algeria, Bruce in South Africa or Ross in India; general practitioners like Manson in China, Bancroft in Queensland or Wucherer in Brazil.

Enlarged opportunities for parasitological research first came with the establishment of schools and hospitals for tropical medicine. Until the end of the nineteenth century the only medical school with facilities modelled upon European lines, and yet with opportunities for the study of tropical parasites, was that at the Kasr-el-ain Hospital in Cairo. Here it was that Griesinger, Bilharz and Looss made their great contributions to parasitology.

The first school of tropical medicine in temperate climes was that opened in Liverpool in 1899. Its chief organizer was R. Boyce, the professor of pathology and Ronald Ross was appointed lecturer a month after it opened. The main efforts of the school went at first into testing in the field Ross's ideas on the eradication of malaria by destroying the vector but it was from this school that Dutton went to identify the first human trypanosome, *T. gambiense* and it was in the blood of a patient under Ross that Stephens discovered the second human trypanosome, *T. rhodesiense*.

The London School of Tropical Medicine developed from two sources under the hand of Sir Patrick Manson. From his " muck-room ", as his laboratory at his home was known, and the Seaman's Hospital at Greenwich. The Seaman's Hospital was descended from the old floating hulk, the Dreadnought Hospital, to which George Busk had been surgeon and it was there he had discovered *Fasciolopsis buskii.* The London school opened some seven months after that at Liverpool and amongst the first parasitological discoveries made there was that of the embryos of *Wuchereria bancrofti* in the proboscis of the mosquito by George Low.[277]

Following the British example other countries also soon established schools of tropical medicine and parasitology. The French Institut de Médecine Coloniale, founded largely by the efforts of R. Blanchard, opened in 1902. The course of instruction given there lasted 10 weeks, covering bacteriology, pathology and clinical work. Blanchard himself gave 21 lectures and a similar number of practical classes on parasitology.[278]

The original Pasteur Institute was founded in 1888 in Paris. But Pasteur encouraged his pupils to go abroad and found more such institutes. The earliest of these was that founded by Calmette in 1889, at Saigon. The first Pasteur Institute in French North Africa was set up, in 1893, at Tunis. Workers in these institutes investigated a wide range of topics in tropical biology and medicine but, inevitably, much of the work was parasitological.[279]

Mr. Henry Wellcome endowed a laboratory for tropical medicine at the Gordon College in Khartoum. It was opened in 1904 with Balfour as its first director. This establishment possessed a floating laboratory on the Nile named the " Culex " which was said to be " well-nigh as ubiquitous as its namesake ". During the first year of the laboratories' existence much parasitological work was done including an investigation of eosinophilia in schistosomiasis and dracontiasis. The Wellcome laboratory soon attracted many able volunteer workers including the Bruces, on their way home from Uganda.[280]

An important centre for parasitological research was developed at Cambridge by G. H. Nuttall. Nuttall who came of a Lancashire family, was born in 1862 in San Francisco where his father practised medicine. Nuttall obtained his M.D. at the University of California in 1884 and then worked in the biology department of Johns Hopkins University. Whilst on study leave in Germany in 1895 he married a German lady and, partly because his father-in-law was unwilling for his daughter to live in so far off a place as Baltimore, Nuttall decided not to accept the charge of the Johns Hopkins Hygiene Department but to establish himself in England. He went to Cambridge in 1899, first as lecturer in bacteriology, but in 1906 he was appointed Quick professor of biology. The Quick Chair was founded, by F. J. Quick, barrister and tea merchant, for the study of " protozoa especially such as cause disease " but in 1920 this was altered, at Nuttall's suggestion, to the " study of parasitology ". At first, the department was housed in a large, noisy, ill-heated and ill-ventilated corner room in the medical school.

But Nuttall attracted a distinguished staff, all of whom worked on very small grants from outside sources for, beyond the professor's stipend, the Quick endowment provided but £300 a year for expenses. In 1919 Nuttall wrote a pamphlet on "The need of an institute for parasitological research in Cambridge" and as a result Mr. and Mrs. Molteno provided £36,000 to build and endow the Molteno Institute. To this Institute Nuttall devoted the remainder of his life. He attracted able workers, built up its scientific collections and donated his own library. Nor was he unmindful of the history of his chosen subject for he collected portraits of famous parasitologists and published a number of interesting biographical notices in *Parasitology,* a journal which he himself founded in 1908.[281]

There is no surer sign that a subject has "come of age" than when it shows itself able to support one or more journals exclusively devoted to it. The earliest journal devoted entirely to parasitology was the *Archives de parasitologie* founded in 1898. This excellent publication continued to appear until 1919 and, besides reporting new discoveries, contained a number of historical articles and some of the best biographical notices of distinguished parasitologists to be found in the literature. It is of interest that although this book constitutes the first attempt to trace the overall history of parasitology, parasitologists have never lacked those among their number with historical interests. To such parasitologists as Davaine, Cobbold, Nuttall, Blanchard and Hoeppli, the present writer's debt is evident on almost every page.

Prior to 1850 there was no noteworthy student of parasitology in the United States. The founder of American parasitology was Joseph Leidy of the University of Pennsylvania. He remained the solitary American parasitologist for 20 years. Leidy's work covered a wide area of natural history and, indeed, he is chiefly famous as a paleontologist. However, his discovery of *Trichinella spiralis* in pork in 1846, his monograph *The Flora and Fauna within Living Animals* in 1851, as well as some hundred parasitological notes constituted notable contributions. At the opening of the twentieth century parasitology as a separate scientific discipline was in the hands of zoologists such as H. B. Ward of the University of Nebraska and C. W. Stiles of the

Public Health Service, both men, incidentally, pupils of R. Leuckart. In 1910 the Helminthological Society of Washington was formed which later became the nucleus of the American Society of Parasitologists which was founded in 1925, H. B. Ward being the first president.

H. B. Ward obtained his Ph.D. from Harvard in 1892 and held a variety of teaching and administrative positions in the Universities of Nebraska and Michigan before becoming professor of zoology at the University of Illinois in 1909. He was part-author, with G. C. Whipple of the well-known book *Fresh-water Biology* and trained many parasitologists. Eight of his pupils subsequently became presidents of the American Society of Parasitologists. Influenced by Nuttall's *Parasitology,* Ward, in 1914, founded the *Journal of Parasitology* as a quarterly devoted to medical zoology. There were 195 subscribers for volume I and the subscription list rose to 600 by volume XVI. The articles published cover a wide range with helminthology predominating. The American Society of Parasitologists used Ward's journal and eventually, in 1932, after many years of negotiation with Ward, took it over from him.[282]

The discoveries of Laveran, Ross and Bruce towards the end of the nineteenth century led to such an expansion of protozoology that it became necessary to split off this branch of parasitology. In 1903 the Imperial Health Office in Berlin decided to found a division of protozoology and Fritz Schaudinn was put in charge. In 1905 it was decided to establish separate departments at the London School of Tropical Medicine. C. M. Wenyon, a 27-year-old son of a doctor working in China, was made director of the protozoology department. Wenyon had studied zoology at the Yorkshire College, Leeds, and at University College, London, and had qualified in medicine from Guy's Hospital in 1904. He spent much of his time working abroad on a variety of topics and in 1914 transferred to the Wellcome Bureau of scientific research. In 1926 he published the most comprehensive and best book on protozoology in any language. This monumental work, which took six years to write, ran to over 1,400 pages, and gave an account of the state of parasitic protozoology as it stood at the beginning of 1926. Following the publication of this great work, Wenyon was elected F.R.S. He died in 1948.

In 1906 the first university chair of protozoology was established in London in connection with the Lister Institute. Ronald Ross applied for the position and was somewhat aggrieved at not being appointed.[283] The first incumbent was E. A. Minchin. Minchin had been brought up in India where he studied natural history rather than played games because of a physical disability. He graduated in zoology at Oxford in 1890 and spent the next nine years there as assistant to Professor Ray Lankester. In 1899 he was appointed professor of zoology at University College, London, and it was from this post that he was translated to the new chair of Protozoology. In 1905 Minchin spent a year in Uganda studying trypanosomes and tsetse-flies in relation to sleeping-sickness. He made a detailed study of the anatomy of the tsetse-fly and demonstrated that it carried species of trypanosomes quite unrelated to sleeping-sickness. This visit to Uganda determined the course of the rest of his life's work which was largely on trypanosomes.[284]

REFERENCES

1. Hoeppli, R. (1959). *Parasites and parasitic infections in early medicine and science,* p. 2. Singapore: University of Malaya Press.
2. Ibid., p. 8.
3. Adams, F. (1844). *The seven books of Paulus Aegineta,* p. 150. London: Sydenham Society.
4. Hoeppli, R. (1959). op. cit., p. 8.
5. Adams, F. (1856). *The extant works of Aretaeus the Cappadocian,* p. 337. London: Sydenham Society.
6. Adams, F. (1844). op. cit., p. 138.
7. Hoeppli, R. (1959). op. cit., p. 18.
8. Ibid., p. 23.
9. Ibid., p. 32.
10. Ibid., p. 69.
11. Ibid., p. 86.
12. Ibid., p. 151.
13. Willis, R. (1847). *The works of William Harvey,* p. 427. London: Sydenham Society.
14. Meyer, A. W. (1939). *The rise of embryology,* p. 41. Stanford University Press.
15. Bodenheimer, F. S. (1958). *The history of biology,* p. 263. London: Dawson.
16. Hoeppli, R. (1959). op. cit., p. 134.
17. Meyer, A. W. (1939). op. cit., p. 42.
18. Lowthrop, J. (1722). *The philosophical transactions and collections . . .* Abridged, p. 121. London.
19. Meyer, A. W. (1939) op. cit., p. 43.
20. Ibid., p. 28 .
21. Andry, N. (1718). *De la génération des vers dans le corps de l'homme,* p. 24, Paris: Laurent d'Houry.
22. Hoeppli, R. (1959). op. cit., p. 98.
23. Bloch, M. (1788). *Traité de la génération des vers des intestines et des vermifuges,* p. 83. Strasbourg: Treuttel.
24. Brera, V. L. (1804). *Traité des maladies vermineuses,* p. 125. Paris: Crochard.
25. Hoeppli, R. (1959). op. cit., p. 153.
26. Meyer, A. W. (1939). op. cit., p. 43.
27. *Arch. Parasit.* (1898). *1, p.* 420.
28. Andry, N. (1718). op. cit., p. 7.
29. Ibid., p. 76.
30. Ibid., p. 108.
31. Benivieni, A. (1954). *The hidden causes of disease,* p. 23. Transl. C. Singer. Springfield: Thomas.
32. Andry, N. (1718). op. cit., p. 97.
33. Smith, C. H. (1839). *Memoir of P. S. Pallas* in volume 25 of The Naturalists Library Edinburgh.
34. Leuckart, R. (1886). *The parasites of man,* p. 333. Transl. W. E. Hoyle. Edinburgh: Pentland.
35. Cobbold, R. (1864). *Entozoa; an introduction to the study of helminthology,* p. 236. London: Groombridge.
36. Nordenskiold, E. (1946). *The history of biology,* p. 352. Transl. L. B. Eyre. New York: Knopf.

37. HUARD, P. & THÉODORIDÈS, J. (1959). *Biol. méd. (Paris)*, *48*, 1.
38. BAILLIE, M. (1797). *The morbid anatomy of some of the most important parts of the human body*, p. 190. London: Johnson.
39. NORDENSKIOLD, E. (1946). op. cit., p. 418.
40. STEENSTRUP, J. S. (1845). *On the alternation of generations*, p. 13. Transl. G. Busk. London: Ray Society.
41. Ibid., p. 26.
42. Ibid., p. 36.
43. Ibid., p. 58.
44. Ibid., p. 69.
45. Ibid., p. 71.
46. Ibid., p. 74.
47. Ibid., p. 94.
48. Ibid., p. 100.
49. HUARD, P. & THÉODORIDÈS, J. (1959). op. cit., p. 75.
50. THÉODORIDÈS, J. (1961). *Arch. Int. Claude Bernard*, *1*.
51. FOSTER, W. D. (1961). *Med. Hist.*, *5*, 341.
52. ADAMS, F. (1844). *The seven books of Paulus Aegineta*, vol. 2, p. 139. London: Sydenham Society.
53. HOEPPLI, R. (1959). *Parasites and parasitic infections in early medicine and science*, p. 18. Singapore: Malaya University Press.
54. LEUCKART, R. (1886). *The parasites of man*, p. 410. Transl. W. E. Hoyle. Edinburgh: Pentland.
55. LOWTHROP, J. (1722). *The philosophical transactions and collections*, abridged, vol. 3, p. 121. London.
56. LEUCKART, R. (1868). op. cit., p. 414.
57. NORDENSKIOLD, N. E. (1946). *The history of biology*, p. 243. Transl. L. B. Eyre. New York: Knopf.
58. LEUCKART, R. (1886). op. cit., p. 416.
59. Ibid., p. 417.
60. Ibid., p. 421.
61. MUNK, W. (1878). *The roll of the Royal College of Physicians of London*, vol. I, p. 426. London: Longman.
62. LOWTHROP, J. (1722). op. cit., p. 121.
63. ANDRY, N. (1718). *De la génération des vers dans le corps de l'homme*, p. 77. Paris: Laurent d'Houry.
64. BLOCH, M. (1788). *Traité de la génération des vers des intestines et des vermifuges*, p. 50. Strasbourg: Treuttel.
65. LEUCKART, R. (1886). op. cit., p. 315.
66. KUCHENMEISTER, F. (1857). *The animal and vegetable parasites of the human body*, vol. 1, p. 13. London: Sydenham Society.
67. HOEPPLI, R. (1959). op. cit., p. 9.
68. KUCHENMEISTER, F. (1857). op. cit., p. 16.
69. OSLER, W. (1908). *An Alabama student and other biographical essays*, p. 80. Oxford University Press.
70. KUCHENMEISTER, F. (1857). op. cit., p. 15.
71. HOEPPLI, R. (1959). op. cit., p. 477.
72. DONLEY, J. E. (1909). *Johns Hopk. Hosp. Bull.*, *20*, 1.
73. KUCHENMEISTER, F. (1857). op. cit. p. 17.
74. Ibid., p. 19.
75. Ibid., p. 19.
76. Ibid., p. 22.
77. Ibid., p. 24.
78. NORDENSKIOLD, E. (1946). op. cit., p. 417.

79. LEUCKART, R. (1886). op. cit., p. 334.
80. KUCHENMEISTER, F. (1857). op. cit., p. 27.
81. Ibid., p. 115.
82. LEUCKART, R. (1886). op. cit., p. 331.
83. KUCHENMEISTER, F. (1857). op. cit., p. 31.
84. MORGAGNI, J. B. (1769). *The seats and cause of disease investigated by anatomy*, vol. 2, p. 326. Transl. B. Alexander. London: Millar & Cadell.
85. LEUCKART, R. (1886). op. cit., p. 583.
86. BAILLIE, M. (1793). *The morbid anatomy of some of the most important parts of the human body*, p. 224. London: Johnson.
87. HUARD, F. & THÉODORIDÈS, J. (1959). Cinq parasitologistes meconnus. *Biol. med. (Paris)*, *48*, 55.
88. BRIGHT, R. (1837). *Guy's Hosp. Rep.* 2, 432.
89. LEUCKART, R. (1886). op. cit., p. 582.
90. KUCHENMEISTER, F. (1857). op. cit., p. 233.
91. Ibid., p. 193.
92. LEUCKART, R. (1886). op. cit., p. 593.
93. FOUNTAIN, A. E. (1961). *J. Helminth.* Leiper suppl. p. 77.
94. THUDICUM, J. L. W. (1864). *Seventh report of the medical officer to the Privy Council*, p. 465. London.
95. LEUCKART, R. (1886). op. cit., p. 476.
96. COBBOLD, T. S. (1864). *Entozoa*, p. 241. London: Groombridge.
97. COBBOLD, T. S. (1879). *Parasites*, p. 79. London: Churchill.
98. LEWIS, T. R. (1888). *Physiological and pathological researches*, p. 502. London.
99. COBBOLD, T. S. (1879). op. cit., p. 76.
100. LEUCKART, R. (1886). op. cit., p. 641.
101. THUDICUM, J. L. W. (1864). op cit., p. 331.
102. FOUNTAIN, A. E. (1961). op. cit., p. 77.
103. COBBOLD, T. S. (1864). op. cit., p. 282.
104. COBBOLD, T. S. (1879). op. cit., p. 123.
105. HOEPPLI, R. (1950). op. cit., p. 32.
106. *Phil. Trans. Roy. Soc.* (1700). 22, 571.
107. Ibid., 22, 509.
108. Ibid. (1704). *24*, 1522.
109. DAVAINE, C. (1860). *Traité des entozoaires*, p. 251. Paris: Baillière.
110. DUJARDIN, F. (1945). *Histoire naturelle des helminthes ou vers intestinaux*, p. 310. Paris: Roret.
111. *Quart. J. micr. Sci.* (1883) *23*, 99.
112. HOEPPLI, R. (1959). op. cit., p. 5.
113. *J. R. Army med. Cps* (1951). *25*, 1.
114. *Z. wiss. Zool.* (1853). *4*, 53.
115. *Parasitology* (1924). *16*, 332.
116. *J. R. Army med. Cps* (1915). *25*, 1.
117. *Brit. med. J.* (1872). 2, 89.
118. *Lancet* (1864). *1*, 156.
119. COBBOLD, T. S. (1879). op. cit., p. 52.
120. *J. R. Army med. Cps* (1915). *25*, 1.
121. *Lancet* (1893). 2, 621.
122. *Lancet* (1891). 2, 480.
123. *Arch. Parasit. (Paris)* (1907). *11*, 423.
124. *J. Path. Bact.* (1894). 2, 52.
125. *J. R. Army med. Cps* (1951). *25*, 1.
126. BRAUN, M. (1906). *The animal parasites of man*, p. 181. Transl. P. Flake Bale. London: Bale and Danielsson.
127. MANSON, P. (1905). *Lectures on tropical diseases*, p. 54. London: Constable.

128. *J. trop. Med.* (1907). *10*, 303.
129. *Ann. trop. Med.* (1909). *2*, 153.
130. *J. trop. Med.* (1909). *12*, 1.
131. Rogers, L. & McGaw, J. W. D. (1935). *Tropical medicine*, 2nd ed., p. 400. London: Churchill.
132. *Proc. R. Soc. Med.* (1915). *9*, 145.
133. Cobbold, T. S. (1869). op. cit., p. 4.
134. *Lond. med. Gaz.* (1833). *11*, 605.
135. Paget, S. (1901). *Memoirs and letters of Sir James Paget*, p. 55. London: Longmans, Green.
136. *Lond. med. Gaz.* (1835). *16*, 190.
137. Ibid. (1836). *17*, 382.
138. Dujardin, F. M. (1945). op. cit., p. 294.
139. Privy Council (1865). *Seventh report of the medical officer*, p. 352.
140. Kuchenmeister, F. (1856). op. cit., p. 352.
141. Privy Council (1865). *Seventh report of the medical officer*, p. 356.
142. Bloomfield, A. L. (1960). *A bibliography of internal medicine—selected diseases*, p. 295. University of Chicago Press.
143. Privy Council (1865). *Seventh report of the medical officer*, p. 348.
144. Osler, W. (1920). *Principles and practice of medicine*, 8th ed., p. 303. London: Appleton.
145. Stoll, N. R. (1947). *J. Parasit. 33*, 1.
146. Scott, H. H. (1939). *A history of tropical medicine*, vol. 2, p. 840. Baltimore: Williams & Wilkins.
147. Hoeppli, R. (1959). *Parasites and parasitic infections in early medicine and science*, p. 493. Singapore: University of Malaya Press.
148. Braun, M. (1906). *The animal parasites of man*, 3rd ed., p. 328. London: Bale and Danielsson.
149. Hirsch, A. (1885). *Handbook of geographical and historical pathology*, vol. 2, p. 313. Transl. C. Creighton. London: New Sydenham Society.
150. Galli-Valesco, B. (1903). *Arch. Parasitol. 7*, 138.
151. Pruner-Bey, F. Biography by Gurlt, E. & Hirsch, A. " Biographischer Lexikon " Vienna. 1886. Vol. 4, p. 635.
152. Griesinger, W. G. Biography—Ibid., vol. 2, p. 648.
153. Davaine, C. (1860). *Traité des entozoaires*, p. 117. Paris: Baillière.
154. Cobbold, T. S. (1879). op. cit., p. 211.
155. Scott, H. H. (1934). op. cit.
156. Boycott, A. E. & Haldane, J. S. (1903). *J. Hyg. 3*, 95.
157. Boycott, A. E. & Haldane, J. S. (1904). *J. Hyg. 4*, 73.
158. Bayles, H. A. (1924). *Parasitology 16*, 335.
159. Boycott, A. E. & Haldane, J. S. (1904). op. cit., p. 73.
160. Bentley, C. A. (1902). *Brit. med. J. 1*, 190.
161. Scott, H. H. (1939). op. cit., p. 840.
162. Adams, F. (1856). op. cit., p. 368.
163. Adams, F. (1844). op. cit., p. 5.
164. Strong, R. P. (1945). *Stitt's tropical diseases*, 7th ed., p. 1297. London: Lewis.
165. Cobbold, T. S. (1878). *J. Linn. Soc. 14*, 356.
166. Lewis, T. R. (1888). *Physiological and pathological researches*, p. xxiii. London.
167. Lewis, T. R. Ibid., p. 503.
168. Alcock, A. & Manson-Bahr, P. (1927). *The life and work of Sir Patrick Manson*, p. 18. London: Cassell.
169. *Customs Gazette Med. Rep.* (1871). 1.
170. Ibid., 10 (1876). 1.

REFERENCES

171. Alcock, A. & Manson-Bahr, P. (1927). op. cit., p. 18.
172. Ibid., p. 75.
173. Cobbold, J. S. (1878). *J. Linn. Soc. 14,* 356.
174. *Lancet* (1877). *2,* 71.
175. Ibid., p. 453.
176. Ibid., p. 495.
177. Alcock, A. & Manson-Bahr, P. (1927). op. cit., p. 43.
178. *Lancet* (1878). *1,* 440.
179. Cobbold, J. S. (1874). *J. Linn. Soc. 14,* 356.
180. *Customs Gazette Med. Rep.* (1877).
181. Lewis, T. R. (1888). op. cit., p. 620.
182. Alcock, A. & Manson-Bahr, P. (1927). op. cit., p. 58.
183. Ibid., p. 51.
184. *Lancet* (1881). *2,* 707.
185. *Customs Gazette Med. Rep.* (1882). *23,* 1.
186. Alcock, A. & Manson-Bahr, P. (1927). op. cit., p. 191.
187. *Brit. med. J.* (1900). *1,* 328.
188. Ibid. (1900). *1,* 1457.
189. Ibid. (1900). *2,* 1306.
190. Cobbold, T. S. (1864). op. cit., p. 375.
191. Numbers 21, verse 6.
192. Cobbold, T. S. (1864). op. cit., p. 375.
193. Hoeppli, R. (1959). op. cit., p. 8.
194. Paulus Agineta. op. cit., p. 150.
195. Davaine, C. (1860). op. cit., p. 698.
196. Lowthrop, J. (1722). op. cit., *3,* p. 138.
197. *Edinb. med. J.* (1805). *1,* 284.
198. Ibid. (1806). *2,* 145.
199. Ibid. (1821). *17,* 96.
200. *Med. Times* (1846). *14,* 130.
201. Kuchenmeister, F. (1857). op. cit., p. 400.
202. Cobbold, T. S. (1864). op. cit., p. 387.
203. Cobbold, T. S. (1879). op. cit., p. 223.
204. Alcock, A. & Manson-Bahr, P. (1927). op. cit., p. 193.
205. Braun, M. (1906). op. cit., p. 282.
206. Manson, P. (1909). *Tropical diseases,* 4th ed., p. 674. London: Cassell.
207. Alcock, A. & Manson-Bahr, P. (1927). op. cit., p. 193.
208. Dobell, C. (1932). *Antony van Leeuwenhoek and his little animals,* p. 217. London: Staples Press.
209. Dujardin, M. F. (1845). op. cit., p. 637.
210. Donné, A. (1837). *Recherces microscopiques sur la nature des mucus.* Paris.
211. Leuckart, R. (1886). op. cit., p. 202.
212. Valentin, G. (1841). *Arch. d. J. Müller,* p. 435.
213. *Lancet* (1883). *1,* 966.
214. *Lancet* (1898). *2,* 1511.
215. *C. R. Acad. Sci. (Paris)* (1843). p. 1134.
216. Lewis, T. R. (1888). *Physiological and pathological researches,* p. 604. London.
217. Crookshank, E. M. (1896). *A Textbook of bacteriology,* 4th ed., p. 593. London: Lewis.
218. Rogers, L. (1904). *Brit. med. J. 2,* 1454.
219. Laveran, A. (1892). *Arch. med. Exper., p.* 257.
220. Bruce, D. (1915). *Lancet 1,* 1323.
221. Austen, E. E. (1903). *Monograph of the tsetse-fly.* London.
222. Bruce, D. (1897). *Further report on the tsetse-fly disease.* London: Harrison.
223. *Brit. med. J.* (1906). *1,* 31.

224. *Brit. med. J.* (1902). *2,* 881.
225. Ibid. (1903). *1,* 1249.
226. Ibid. (1905). *1,* 1020.
227. *Brit. med. J.* (1903). *1,* 721.
228. WIGGINS, C. A. (1960). *E. Afr. med. J. 37,* 699.
229. CASTELLANI, A. (1960). *Microbes, men and monarchs,* p. 31. London: Gollancz.
230. DAVIES, J. N. P. (1962). *E. Afr. med. J. 39,* 146.
231. *Rep. Roy. Soc.* Sleeping-sickness Commission (1903). *3,* 3.
232. Ibid. (1903). *1,* 2.
233. Ibid. (1903). *4,* 2.
234. Ibid. (1907). *8,* 5.
235. Ibid. (1909). *10,* 46.
236. CARPENTER, G. D. H. (1920). *A naturalist on Lake Victoria.* London: Fisher-Unwin.
237. *Lancet* (1953). *1,* 300.
238. *Rep. Roy. Soc.* Sleeping-sickness Commission (1902). *13,* 1.
239. *Proc. R. Soc. B.* (1910). *83,* 28.
240. Ibid. (1913). *86,* 269.
241. *Trans. R. Soc. trop. Med. Hyg.* (1920). *14,* 31.
242. *Trans. R. Soc. trop. Med. Hyg.* (1927). *21,* 187.
243. *Ann. trop. Med. Parasitol.* (1929). *23,* 37.
244. FISKE, W. F. (1927). *A History of sleeping-sickness and reclamation in Uganda.* Entebbe.
245. *Sleeping-sickness Bureau Bull.* (1909). *2,* 117.
246. *Trop. Dis. Bull.* (1934). *31,* 757.
247. OSLER, W. (1897). *Principles and practice of medicine,* p. 147. London: Pentland.
248. ANNESLEY, J. (1841). *Diseases of India,* 2nd ed., p. 384. London: Longman.
249. DOBELL, C. (1919). *The Amoebae living in man,* p. 8. New York: Wood.
250. LOSCH, F. (1875). *Arch. Path. Anat. 65,* 196.
251. DOBELL, C. (1919). Ibid., p. 22.
252. CUSHING, H. (1926). op. cit., vol. I, p. 326.
253. OSLER, W. (1890). *Johns Hopk. Hosp. Bull. 1,* 53.
254. COUNCILMAN & LAFLEUR (1891). *Johns Hopk. Hosp. Rep. 2,* 393.
255. QUINKE & ROOS (1893). *Berl. klin. Wschr. 30,* 1089.
256. DOBELL, C. (1919). Ibid., p. 11.
257. *Johns Hopk. Hosp. Bull.* (1908). *19,* 169.
258. DOBELL, C. (1919). Ibid., p. 27.
259. *Deutsch med. Wschr.* (1903). *29,* 267.
260. DOBELL, C. (1919). Ibid., p. 11.
261. *Brit. med. J.* (1902). 2, 841.
262. *Lancet* (1922). *1,* 463.
263. ROGERS, L. (1950). *Happy toil,* p. 67. London: J. Muller.
264. *J. infect. Dis.* (1908). *5,* 324.
265. *Brit. med. J.* (1913). 2, 1287.
266. MANSON, P. (1909). op. cit., p. 443.
267. Ibid., p. 482.
268. *Philipp. J. Sci.* (1911). *6,* 259.
269. Ibid. (1913). *8,* 253.
270. *J. R. Army med. Cps* (1917). *28,* 1.
271. *J. Path. Bact.* (1918). 22, 22.
272. CLARK, P. F. (1959). *J. Hist. med. allied Sci. 14,* 490.
273. BULLOCH, W. (1935). *J. Path. Bact. 40,* 621.
274. SMITH, T. & KILBORNE, F. L. (1893). *Investigations into the nature, causation and prevention of Texas or southern cattle fever.* Washington: Government Printing Press.
275. COWDRY, E. V. & HAM, A. W. (1932). *Parasitology, 24,* 1.

REFERENCES

276. Cornil, A. V. & Babes, V. (1890). *Les Bactéries,* vol. 2, p. 567. Paris: F. Alcan.
277. Manson-Bahr, P. (1956). *History of the School of Tropical Medicine in London.* London: Lewis.
278. *Arch. Parasitol.* (1902). *6,* 585.
279. *Notice sur L'Institut Pasteur d'Algerie* (1934).
280. Balfour, A. (1904). *Report of the Wellcome Tropical Research Laboratories at the Gordon Memorial College, Khartoum.*
281. *Parasitology* (1922). *14,* 97.
282. *J. Parasitol.* (1962). *48,* 641.
283. Ross, R. (1923). *Memoirs,* p. 494. London: Murray.
284. *J. Path. Bact.* (1925). *20,* 361.

INDEX OF PERSONAL NAMES

INDEX OF PERSONAL NAMES

Printed by The Central Press (Aberdeen) Ltd.